A Jar of Seed-Corn

Portrait of an island farm

Jocelyn Rendall

A Jar of Seed-Corn

Portrait of an island farm

by

Jocelyn Rendall

"When tillage begins, other arts follow. The farmers therefore are the founders of human civilisation."
(Daniel Webster 1782-1852)

The Orcadian Limited,
Orkney

2002

ISBN 1 902957 16 4

Printed and published in Orkney
The Orcadian Limited, Hell's Half Acre,
Kirkwall, Orkney, Scotland
Tel 01856 879000: Fax 01856 879001: www.orcadian.co.uk

In memory of Chris Meek,
who loved the island, and always
brought laughter with her

Contents

Cover photographs. Front: Main photograph: The roof of the mill-tramp at Holland Farm. Insets, left to right: Thomas Traill of Holland; Holland House; John Rendall of Holland building dykes; Jeremiah and Isabella Seatter of Hundland, crofters on the Holland Estate; lifting tatties beside St Tredwell's Loch; Neil Rendall taking rams to the Holm of Papay; Aberdeen Angus cattle on the shore of St Tredwell's Loch. **Back:** Jim Wallace MP joins Orkney farmers' demonstration in Broad Street, Kirkwall, December, 1997; the author with the first pedigree heifer of the Micklegarth Abedeen Angus herd; Holmie Day "sheepies" being carried to the boat after clipping.

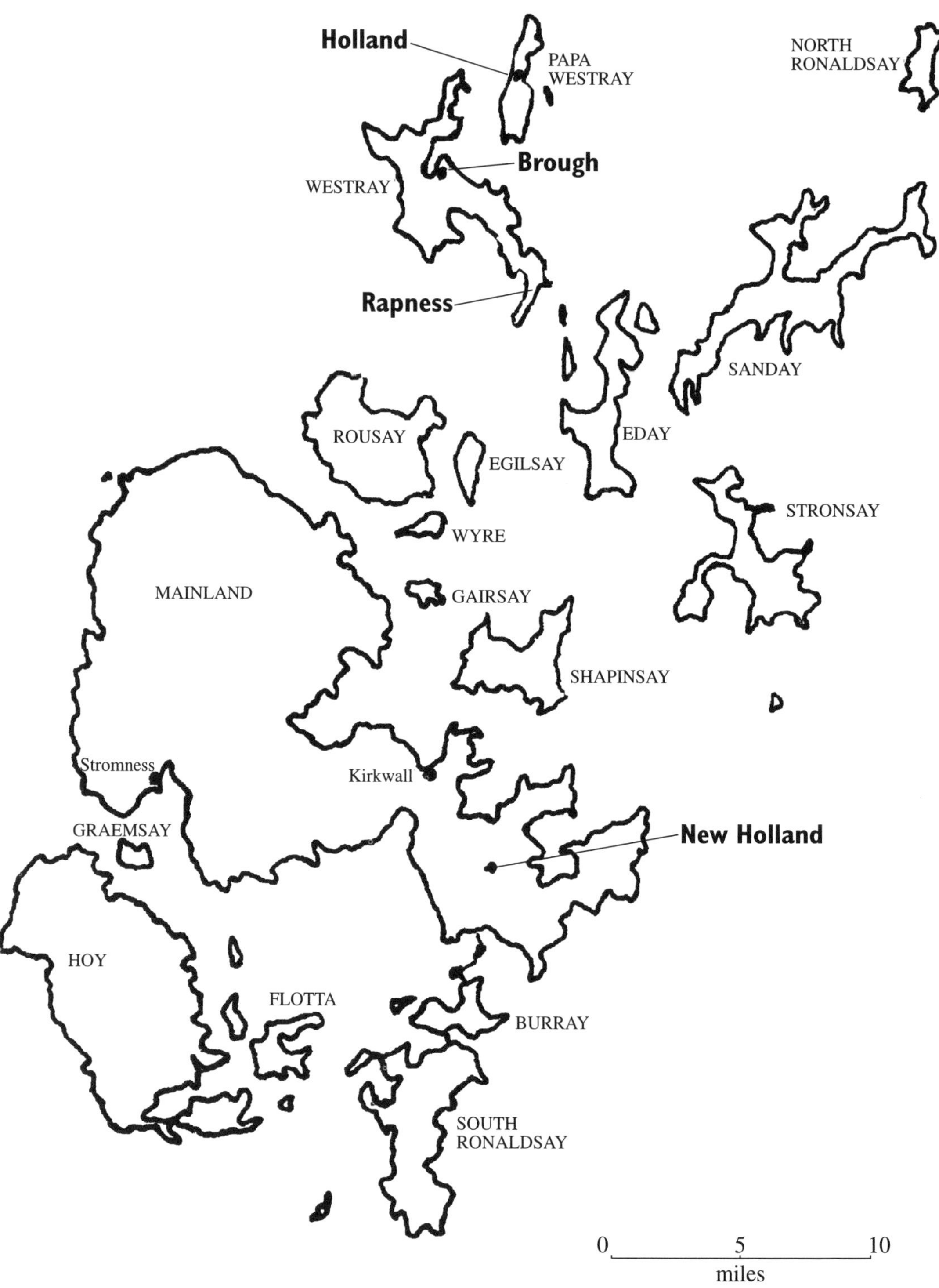

A map of Orkney showing the principal farms of the Holland Estate.

Acknowledgements

I would like to thank all those people who helped me to gather the material for this book and to shape it for publication. I am especially indebted to Willie Thomson for encouraging the project from the beginning. Without him it would never have got off the ground and I would certainly not have ventured into the quagmire territory of the medieval Rentals. Professor Alexander Fenton, Dr Ray Fereday and Elizabeth Beaton kindly read drafts of the manuscript, gave valuable advice and attempted to steer me from historical error and infelicities of syntax. My patient publisher James Miller of *The Orcadian* had a hard time controlling runaway hyphens and opinions. The staff at the Orkney Library Archives and Photographic Archives were unfailingly helpful in finding estate maps and documents, disentangling me from microfilm, and lending photographs for publication. The National Farmers' Union, the College of Agriculture and the Auction Mart in Kirkwall all supplied me with agricultural statistics. A big thank you to Inga Hourston for her drawings. Most of all, I want to thank John and Annie Jean Rendall of Holland for all their memories, photographs and stories of Holland Farm, and my husband Neil who was the chief encourager, critic, script reader and computer technician. This is for them.

Jocelyn Rendall
2001

Foreword

There is no other Orkney book quite like this one - it is a detailed study of a single farm over the last three centuries. The farm, Holland in Papa Westray, is one of the best farms in the North Isles, and the former owners were important and memorable, although not always models of respectability. The survival of farm accounts, estate maps and other unpublished and published sources has permitted a remarkably detailed reconstruction.

The history of Holland, however, is more than just a study of one farm. The Traills of Holland owned Papay and they had an extensive estate in Westray, so the story of Holland is also the history of Papay, and is important for understanding broader changes in the North Isles. One of the great merits of this books is that it provides concrete examples of so many of the trends which affected modern and pre-modern agriculture throughout Orkney.

Eighteenth century merchant-lairds were Jacobite in their sympathies and constantly at odds with Presbyterian ministers who attempted without much success to curb the landowners' unruly and licentious lifestyle - it was a time when landowners dominated island communities without any real check. They depended on legitimate trade and the profits from smuggling as much as on their rents. Old-style farming was little modified because of the remoteness of Papay from markets, and latterly because of the necessity of accommodating a large kelp-making labour force.

Holland, however, illustrates not only the backwardness of traditional farming, but also the speed and the scale of improvement as the 19th century advanced. Thomas Traill was one of Orkney's foremost improvers: he transformed the landscape by his draining, squaring and enclosing, and his farm-steadings at Holland and at Brough in Westray are among the most impressive in Orkney. Like most lairds he was in financial difficulty in the 1880s when the years of prosperity came to an end, but no one went quite so spectacularly bankrupt as Traill whose debts would have paid the wages of his farm servants a thousand times over. Traill's bankruptcy blighted the farm for the next half-century and there was a very slow recovery from the capital-starved years of stagnation. The difficulties were greater than most farmers faced, but were not altogether untypical of the lean years before the 1939-45 war. The book brings the story up to date by describing modern farming and the quite different set of problems which confront farmers at the beginning of the 21st century.

This is not just the story of the lairds, but also of their farm servants, cottars and crofters - and what a large number of them there once were! In 1841, in addition to the big house, another 11 dwellings crowded round the steading with a total of 72 people and, in addition, there were many others who looked to Holland for casual employment. Thomas Traill's bankruptcy coincided with the crisis in crofting, and the Crofters Commission ordered bigger rent reductions and cancelled a greater proportion of arrears than on any other Orkney estate. As elsewhere in Orkney many crofters applied for enlargements to their crofts at the expense of the big farm. Applications for enlargements were usually refused because farms were subject to leases. At Holland, however, the land was not leased but managed directly by the trust which administered the bankrupt estate, and so it was one of the very few places in Orkney where crofters succeeded in gaining extra land.

Readers will quickly appreciate that Jocelyn Rendall's book is no outsider's view but an account which springs from a commitment to Holland, the island and its people. There is a sense of real continuity with the 250 or so generations which have cultivated the same land since Neolithic farmers first settled at the Knap of Howar, but there is also an awareness that immediate concerns are just as important as anything that has happened in the island's long history.

William P.L. Thomson
2001

Preface

He causeth the grass to grow for the cattle, and herb for the service of man, that he may bring forth food out of the earth.
Psalm 104, v.14

The skyline of Papa Westray, one of the most northerly isles of the Orkney archipelago, is dominated by the mansion and steading of Holland Farm, in its heyday the centre of a large estate which extended across several islands. Ten minutes walk away you find another farmstead in the dunes on the Links of Holland. It is roofless, but its expertly-built stone walls still stand to the door lintels and stone furniture survives in both house and the adjoining workshop or byre. The Knap of Howar is the oldest surviving farmstead in Orkney and the oldest standing house to have been discovered in northern Europe. The farmers who brought the first jar of seed corn to the island settled here about 3,800 BC. They would have found the surrounding land fertile and easy to cultivate; the soil was not too heavy for simple tools of bone and stone and on their fields they grew both barley and wheat and raised cattle and sheep. From their time to ours, perhaps 250 generations of our farming predecessors have ploughed the same fields and tended their crops and livestock on them.

This is a close-up view of one island farm, but Holland is a paradigm, not an exception. Travel to the North Isles of Orkney in the small eight-seater plane that links them to Mainland and you look down on an orderly patchwork of green fields interspersed with farm steadings. It is impossible to be unaware of the extent to which the landscape has been tamed by centuries of agricultural use, or of the significance of farming to the past and present economy. Although windswept and treeless, much of the land is astonishingly fertile and in the long hours of summer daylight crops and grassland flourish despite the often harsh northern climate. Even on the remoter islands there is archaeological evidence that they were settled by farming communities from the 4th millennium BC, when neolithic agriculture supported a substantial population and a well-organised society with the resources to create such magnificent ritual monuments as the Ring of Brodgar or the many complex chambered tombs.

Neolithic field walls revealed below the peat in the hilly areas of Mainland Orkney are traces of the farms that were abandoned - and never reoccupied - when the colder and wetter climate of the 2nd millenium BC forced their owners down to the drier land around the coast. The low, well-drained land of Papay, however, was never overtaken by peat and the Bronze Age gairsty or earthwork dividing the island suggests continued occupation and cultivation. Both sea and land were efficiently exploited for survival by people who inhabited the same sites for century after century, but it seems that in the early Middle Ages significant changes in land management practice allowed production to increase and farming to become a commercial activity.[1]

Orkney's gentle landscape and easy access by sea has always attracted the land-hungry. It is easy to imagine how spacious and attractive the green islands must have seemed to settlers from the rocky seaboard of western Norway, but our perception of Norse colonisation tends to be coloured by the bloodthirsty exploits of the axe-wielding Vikings of *Orkneyinga Saga,* and it is easily overlooked that the Norse also engaged in more interesting and beneficial activities than eviscerating one another. It was farmers who came here in search of corn fields and cattle pasture who developed techniques (possibly learned from their Pictish predecessors) of intensive manuring and cultivation of the soil, generating a surplus of crops and the development of trade in food products. Despite the horned-helmeted figures on the tourist brochures with which we still try to allure visitors, the landscape and history of Orkney was shaped by farmers rather than warriors, and their story also has its epic moments. The most significant revolution on Orkney soil was an agricultural one, and if this was bloodless it was by no means undramatic.

Although the cycles of seed-time and harvest have been repeated down so many centuries, the evolution of agriculture has been far from a gradual and steady process. Rather it could be described as long periods of stasis punctuated by sudden leaps forward and as abrupt reversals. Had one of the farmers from the Knap of Howar been able to take a time-machine trip and visit a tenant farm on Papay in the 18th century, for example, doubtless he would have been astonished at and envious of the metal tools his successors were using, but he would hardly have been impressed by their cattle, rather smaller than his own, or by their dwelling-houses, which probably made the Knap seem commodious in comparison. He might well have been appalled to find them living much closer to starvation, deprived of rights in the land they worked or of the produce of their own labour by an oppressive social system. The landscape that he knew would have been greatly altered by the incursions of the sea, and denuded of its scrubby tree cover, but probably still recognisable. Had he come back, however, in the 1860s, our imaginary ancestor would have been totally bewildered by the violent transformation brought about during the "agricultural revolution". Another century later, the piecemeal arable landscape which that created - the "fold, fallow and plough" of grass, root crops and grain grown in rotation in enclosed fields - was itself transformed by another, "green", revolution.

It is the impact of these changes on the islands' landscape and economy in the 19th and 20th centuries, and the backdrop of agricultural routine that they took place against, that I have focused on in this study of Orkney farming. I have told the story from the point of view of one farm, but the events that shaped Holland's history mirrored those happening on all the other islands. Until a couple of generations ago, almost the whole population of Orkney was directly dependent on agriculture and its pendulum swings between periods of growth, intense inventive energy, optimism and prosperity, and slumps into economic decline, depression and even crisis: hungry times that cannot be explained in terms of the failure of Orkney's fertile land or even its fickle climate alone. It is impossible to chart agricultural development in any time or place in isolation from a web of political circumstance, and while this is painfully obvious today it has probably been true ever since man first adopted the life of the settled agriculturist.

The effects of this momentous decision on human history can be regarded in quite different lights. The quotation from the American lawyer and politician Daniel Webster on the title page summarises the positive view: it was the domestication of plants and animals which transformed small bands of wandering hunter-gatherers into the increasingly large and complex settled communities which created all the cultural achievements of human civilisation. In the *Book of Genesis* man's divinely appointed role is that of cultivator, even in the Garden of Eden. There is, however, a converse, darker view of the neolithic revolution. Farming led to population growth and the development of competitive societies with highly stratified social and political hierarchies. When the primitive "noble savage" first regarded land as a commodity rather than a resource the door was opened to acquisition, greed, oppression, exploitation and conflict. There is truth in both views and societies' philosophers, politicians and conservationists have alternately painted the farmer as hero, victim and villain.

The immediate cause of the serious famines which occurred periodically in Orkney until the 19th century was the failure of the harvests, but the destitution was less the result of poor seasons and inefficient farming than of the burden of rents, land taxes and feu duties which drained the islands' wealth out of the county. The class of powerful merchant lairds who emerged in Orkney in the 17th century amalgamated many farms to create the large estates like Holland, and the original small owner-occupiers or udallers were reduced to tenants, paying for their land in produce and labour. The lairds themselves were paying feu-duties in kind to absentee overlords, and had neither the capital nor the financial incentive to improve the agriculture of island estates so remote from mainland markets. While the rest of Scotland was transformed by the agrarian innovations of the late 18th and early 19th centuries, Orkney farms stagnated in a state unchanged since the Middle Ages.

It was only in the mid 19th century that Orkney's belated Agricultural Revolution brought abrupt modernisation to traditional farming, and a brief "Golden Age" of prosperity to the islands. New systems of husbandry and advances in mechanisation changed farming methods, but it was revolution of a different kind that made the most significant difference to the lives of the small tenants who made up the great majority of the farming population. The radical legislation of the 1886 Crofters Act, enshrining the principle that landowners' property rights were not absolute but limited by the rights of the propertyless to security of home and livelihood, undermined the traditional assumptions which upheld landed estates and altered them as profoundly as enclosures had transformed the landscape.

The break with the past was made irrevocable by the social and economic upheaval of the Great War of 1914-18 which tore apart the pattern of rural life throughout the country. During the Second World War of 1939-45, the military activity which centred on Orkney and the huge numbers of service personnel based here had such an impact on life in the islands that the period has become a historical watershed. Pre-war Orkney farming seems in a remote past glimpsed in sepia photographs, while post-war it has been driven by the whirlwind progress of mechanisation, and complicated by the vast increase in government control (both at national and European level) and, consequently, bureaucracy. Perhaps never before in history has our life been so dislocated from that of our immediate forebears. At the turn of the 21st century the farmer's worst anxiety is less likely to be the unseasonal storm in the hairst than the breakdown of his computer, or nightmares too terrifying to be named but in initials: IACS, CAP, BSE. . .[2]

Orkney's agriculture in the 19th century is well recorded. Several writers deplored the lamentably backward state of farming in the pre-improvements era, and many more discussed and admired the miraculous changes that the "Improvers" brought about. Most of the land was owned by large landowners like the Traills of Holland, with capital and manpower to bring about massive programmes of construction and reclamation. Farming was seen as profitable, fashionable, and a subject of widespread interest. Paradoxically, the more recent past is far less documented. For much of the 20th century Orkney farms were small and suffering from severely depressed farm prices. Mechanisation was happening but change was slow and piecemeal and agriculture had definitely lost its glamour. Even the events that, retrospectively, seem momentous were given oddly little attention at the time. The Journal of the Orkney Agricultural Discussion Society, for example, records many debates on the virtues of the five or the six year crop rotation, or the advantages of silage, but none on the break-up of the large estates and the transition of most Orcadians from tenants to owner-occupiers.

The history of Holland farm is written in stone in its steading, one of the best-preserved in Orkney, with fine buildings of the 17th, 18th and 19th centuries still in use beside those of the late 20th century. In medieval times a modest property on one of the smallest isles, it became the seat of one of the most powerful landholding families in Orkney and the centre of a large estate which included extensive lands on the neighbouring island Westray and also on Mainland Orkney as well as the whole island of Papay. Its 19th-century lairds were among the foremost "Improvers" and in their hands Holland became a model farm, exemplifying the latest theories of the agricultural revolution. With Thomas Traill's bankruptcy in 1886 the family fortunes collapsed, the estate was sequestrated and the farm leased to tenants, and its lands were gradually whittled away by compulsory purchase under the Landholding Acts. When the dust of litigation finally cleared in 1922, the farm had considerably shrunk and the estate had disappeared.

Holland weathered the long years of agricultural depression between the wars in the hands of tenant farmers but since 1954 it has been owned and worked by three generations of the same family. It is their dedication to preserving both the old buildings and the traditions of Holland, while constantly improving it as a modern working farm, that has made Holland the special place it is today, and motivated me to collect the material for this book. Memories of the times closest to us are usually seen as too mundane to be worth recording; imperceptibly they slip over the horizon that divides the present from the past and quietly vanish. The farming routine that John Rendall remembers of 50, or even 30 years ago is of a way of life that is already half-forgotten in a population losing its links with farming and I have realised how alarmingly quickly the pace of change relegates our present to the lumber of the past. With the help of John, Annie Jean and

Neil Rendall, I have tried to capture some of these fugitive memories and record the day-to-day running of an island farm in the second half of the 20th century.

The curved walling of the Knap of Howar sunk into the shore and the corbie-stepped gables of Holland farm punching the skyline are symbols of the long partnership between people and the land on this small corner of the archipelago. It was to celebrate this partnership that I began collecting this anthology of history and reflection, anecdote and image which is the story of Holland, but even as I wrote it the ground shifted under my feet. In the early 1990s most of the families living on Papay were still involved in farming, which at that time was at a high point on fortune's wheel. In the course of the decade both the population and the economics of agriculture changed considerably and, as the last years of the 20th century cast long shadows over the future of farming and of the island, it became increasingly difficult to write without pessimism. My hope is that this will prove unfounded. I did not want to write a valediction but a celebration; a thanks for a place where the cattle still graze where their predecessors have grazed for the last 6,000 years, around the Knap of Howar on the Links of Holland.

The Staigy Hoose *(Inga Hourston)*

I

Island

A most beautiful little isle, rich in excellent corn and luxuriant natural grass. The uncultivated part like a carpet spread with all the flowers in season . . .
The Rev George Low

"Papa Westray" is a relatively modern cartographer's invention. The island has always been known by its inhabitants by the name that the Vikings gave it: Papay, "isle of priests". When they came here in the 9th century they found the place well-populated, and with at least two churches. On the west shore stood St Boniface, a kirk and probably also a monastic complex founded by Picts about a hundred years earlier,[i] and in the small island in the loch the chapel dedicated to St Tredwell, a saint whose healing powers drew pilgrims from far afield to Papay right up to the 18th century.[ii]

St Boniface was built in the midst of a large settlement already some 1,500 years old, its importance as an Iron Age power centre testified by the ruins of a large round-house a stone's throw away.[iii] Landward were fertile corn-growing lands and a few miles west across Papa Sound the fine natural harbour of Pierowall on Westray, where early Norse graves attest its use by contemporary merchant shipping. This was a prime economic and strategic location, commanding the main sea-way to Shetland, and there is no doubt that a church in such a site had been well endowed and protected by the secular hierarchy. It is even possible that St Boniface was the seat of the first bishopric in Orkney.[iv] The existence of such an important church reinforces the impression that even at this time Papay was a valuable estate, its fertile lands a source of wealth and power to its owners.

Although the archaeological evidence of prehistoric Orkney is so rich, the Middle Ages are only occasionally illuminated by historical and literary sources. From *Orkneyinga Saga* we know of Papay's ecclesiastical importance, that it was a place named for its priests and chosen for Earl Rognvald Brusason's burial in 1046, and also that it was part of the estate of "a distinguished woman called Ragna" whose main farm was on North Ronaldsay.[5] We know nothing of the island in later medieval times, until a few glimpses are provided by the rentals which survive from the late 15th and 16th centuries. These record that Papay was divided into two administrative districts, "be-north the yard" and "be-south the yard", and these terms survive into modern times. North and south consisted of two urislands each, the urisland being a district composed of 18 pennylands, the land unit on which skat or land tax was levied. Skat and rent were paid in agricultural produce which was then traded overseas. Under Norse rule there were close economic ties with Norway, Orkney exporting her surplus of grain in return for necessities such as timber. Just as 8th-century Papay was an important link in the religious organisation of the time which saw Christian missionaries like Boniface dispatched all over Dark Age Europe, it would also have been a part of

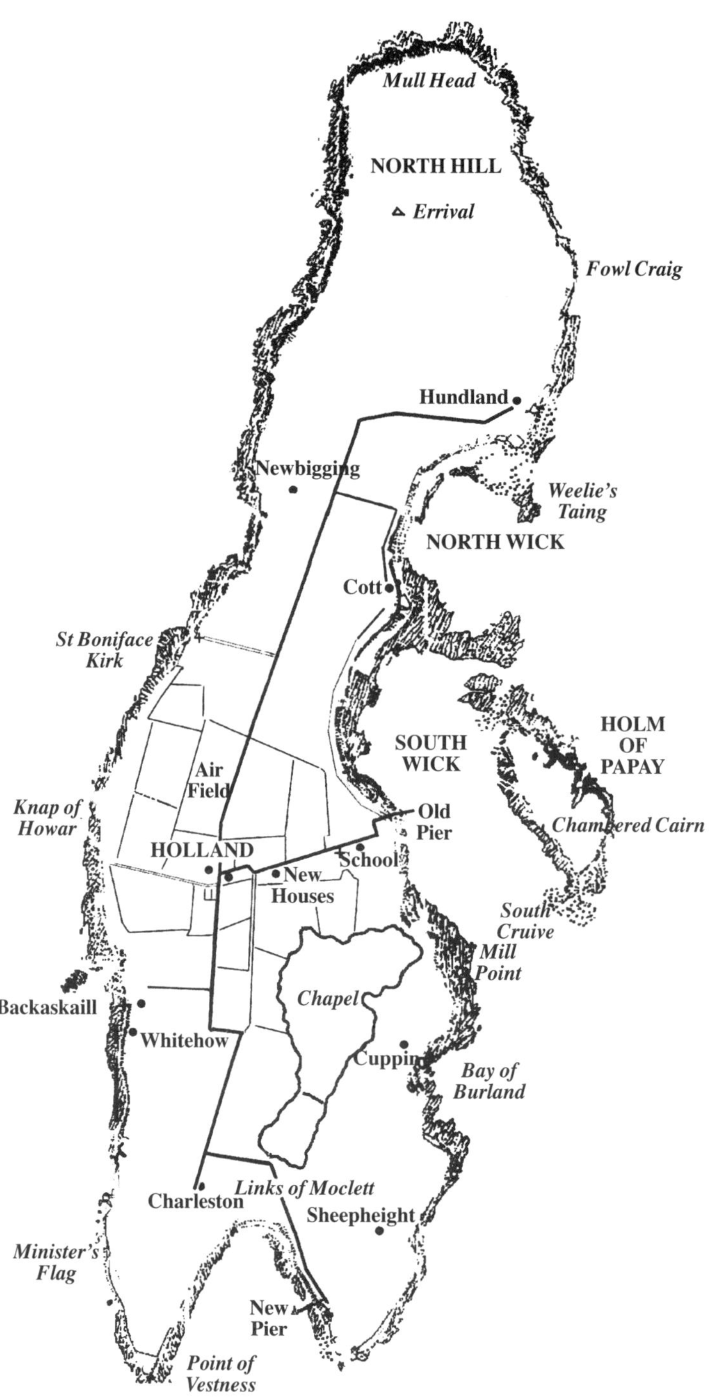

A map of Papa Westray shows Holland situated in a commanding, central position. The island is approximately four and a half miles long and less than a mile wide.

these medieval trade links with the Continent. It is an anachronism to think of this productive and strategically-placed island as remote and peripheral in the past.

In the late Middle Ages, however, Orkney shared with most of Northern Europe a severe economic depression. The population fell drastically due to the Black Death (1347-1351), and continued to fall; grain prices fell to half their previous level and all over the Continent arable land, especially in the more marginal areas, was abandoned in favour of stock-rearing.. Recurrences of plague reduced Norway's population by as much as a third and, due to the lack of demand for grain as well as its own depopulation, Orkney's markets collapsed and an enormous amount of arable land went out of cultivation.[6] In addition, Orkney's agriculture was as vulnerable to European economic pressure then as it is now. The German merchants of the powerful Hanseatic League gained a monopoly of the grain trade in the 15th century and Orkney was squeezed out of the diminished market.

Natural disasters also affected the agriculture. Islands with sandy soils were drastically affected by erosion, possibly caused by a cycle of exceptionally bad weather, or by the introduction of rabbits or a combination of both. In 1492 Lord Henry Sinclair was told that tracts of land in Westray had become useless because the soil was all "blawn till Issland" (blown to Iceland!)[7] and in 1500 the inhabitants of Papay claimed that a third of the island was "all our blawin (over-blown) with wattir et sand" and were allowed a reduction of skat on the eroded lands.[8]

Under Lord Henry's good management there was considerable economic recovery and the abandoned land came back into cultivation. The uncertain climate caused periodic cycles of poor harvests which the inflexible system for collecting rents and skats aggravated into famines, but in most years Orkney was able to produce and export a surplus of oats and bere (a hardy form of barley).[9] Much of this must have come from the agriculturally productive lands of the North Isles, especially Sanday, Stronsay, Westray and Papay. In the mid 17th century this small island was sufficiently attractive for a wealthy and upwardly-mobile soldier of fortune, Colonel Thomas Traill, to choose it as his family seat.

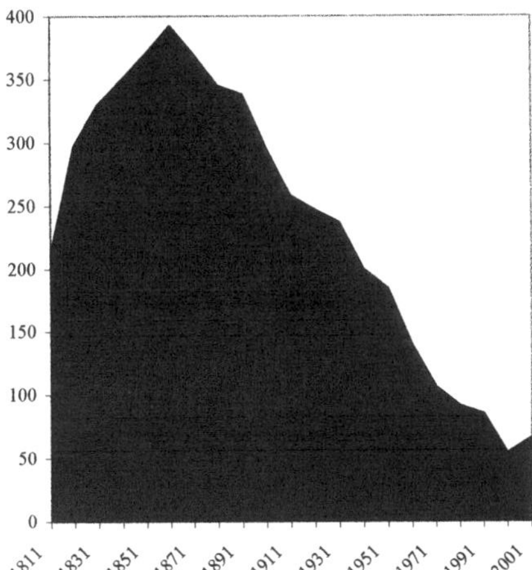

The Population of Papay 1811 - 2001. The decline during the past century is obvious.

Papay was invariably singled out for its lushness in later descriptions of Orkney. In 1778 the Reverend George Low (the minister of Birsay and Harray parishes and also a naturalist), described it as: "a most beautiful little isle, rich in excellent corn and luxuriant natural grass. The uncultivated part like a carpet spread with all the flowers in season."[10] In 1794 the local minister reported that Papay is "a very fertile island, containing some of the best pasture and arable lands in the whole county",[11] and these accounts were written long before the agricultural improvements of the mid 19th century. In August 1804 the traveller Patrick Neill visited this "beautiful little island . . . never did our eyes behold richer tracts of natural clover, red and white. . . the soil is good . . . and clothed with abundant crops of oats, bere and potatoes".[12] The island was always considered a desirable agricultural property, despite its smallness and its lack of a good harbour.

Papay is only four and a half miles long and some 2,500 acres in extent, and along both east and west shores the exposed walls and middens of former settlements - neolithic, medieval or only a century old - testify to the constant efforts of the Atlantic and the North Sea to make it still smaller. Much of the land is fairly level and easily cultivated, rising only gently at the north end to its highest point, Errival, 157 feet above sea-level, and terminated abruptly by the cliffs that fall to the sea at the Mull. From the vantage point of Holland, on the slight crest that runs down the spine of the island, one can see all the other North Isles except Stronsay, hidden behind the flat blur to the south-east that is Sanday. Closer and much more prominent are the Red Heads of Eday, a dark huddle of cliffs suddenly radiant in the light of a summer evening, and west and south our much larger neighbour Westray curves round us with a crescent of fertile farms. On a clear day North Ronaldsay appears to the north-east, or at least the houses do, shimmering on the water without support of land like a convoy of ships, and above Westray the giant windmills on Burgar Hill semaphore to Holland through a dip in the Rousay hills.

Holland stands in the very centre of the island, the road running through the middle of it and marking a neat social divide between the Georgian mansion house on one side and the steading on the other. Its fields slope down to the large expanse of St Tredwell's Loch on the south east, while westward a track runs past the dovecote and between the North-West Toun and the South-West Toun to the Links, where the Knap of Howar lies half-buried above the rocky shore. The northern boundary is the large silage field that doubles as the airfield for the small Islander planes that provide the main passenger link with the Orkney Mainland. To the east beyond the walled garden the "gentry slap", the original gateway to Holland, opens on the road that dips through the island nucleus of shop and school and kirk to the old pier a quarter of a mile distant where, until 1970, the ferry boats docked their cargo once a week, sheltered by the Holm of Papay. This uninhabited island, a neolithic burial-place and summer home for thousands of seabirds, also belongs to Holland, and a flock of native Orkney sheep survive here on sea-ware and 47 acres of thin pasture.

Stone dykes, evidence of a 19th-century laird's passion for "squaring" the landscape, divide Holland's fields into neat parcels, and demarcate them from the lands of the former tenants which did not succumb to enclosure and barbed wire for another hundred years. More dykes divide the northmost farms from 500 acres of rough common grazing. The North Hill is an important Site of Special Scientific Interest for its extensive maritime heath habitat and the rare plants it supports, and vibrant in the nesting season with the sound of skuas and colonies of arctic terns. Auks and kittiwakes gather in noisy congregations on the cliffs at Fowl Craig, but south of this point the coastline softens to wide sweeps of white sand, North Wick and South Wick. Some winter lochans are bright patches of yellow segs in summer, but most of the land is cultivated and scattered with the houses and steadings of small farms.

Or, all too often, the ruins of them. At the turn of the 20th century the island supported about 300 people, and there were still over 40 farms here until the Second World War, but after that the population declined steadily. The 10 and 20 acre farms were amalgamated into larger units and many of the houses abandoned. In 1997 numbers fell to as low as 54 persons and by 2000 there were only half a dozen working farms. The change from sea to road transport, rather than economic hardship, has been the principal factor which has brought about the inexorable drift to Kirkwall which is affecting all the North Isles. For so many seaborne centuries they were situated on the main highways of communication but within a lifetime the motorcar has relegated them to the periphery. It is a sad irony that islands that survived generations of poverty have been emptied by the relative prosperity of recent times. Emigration and retirement from Papay during the 1990s leaves so few farmers that, for the first time in centuries, arable land lies unwanted and pasture grows rank with neglect.

Lush with grass and wild flowers in the summer and often vivid in the winter with the swift changes of the Orkney light on the surrounding sky and sea, Papay is still an exceptionally "beautiful little island". Yet its small community is now strangely vulnerable and hangs on an uncertain future, as stone walls torn from the shoreline by a violent winter storm hang precariously in the space that once was solid ground.

Cuppin *(Inga Hourston)*

THE TRAILLS OF HOLLAND

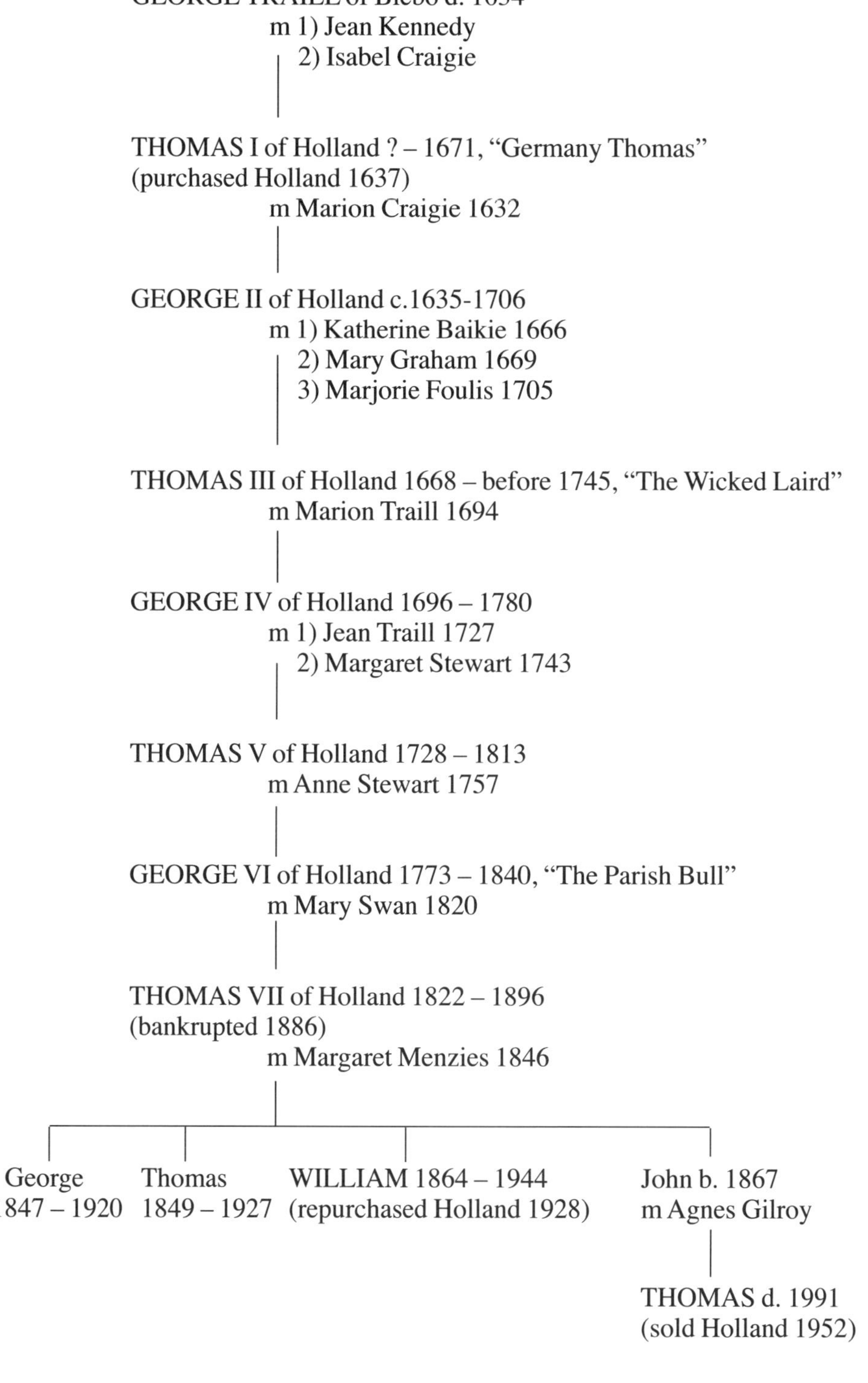

II

Lairds

Traills up the town, Traills down the town, Traills in the middle;
Deil tak the Traills' guts for strings to his fiddle.
Traditional[1]

The name Holland occurs in thirteen islands or Mainland parishes, all in the east of Orkney. Hugh Marwick derived the name from Old Norse *hoy* or high-land[2] which suggests that there was a farm of that name here from the days of Viking settlement, and although Papay's gentle landscape could hardly be described as hilly, the farm does dominate the island from an elevated situation, as its lairds undoubtedly dominated their surrounding tenantry for 250 years. Their story begins in 1637 when an entry in the Register of Sasines of Orkney confirms that John Scollay sold his house Holland in Papa Westray to Thomas Traill.[3]

Orkney in the 17th and 18th centuries was in the hands of just a few large families, most of whom first came to Orkney from Scotland in the 16th century in the wake of the Stewart earls. They drew rent and status from their island estates but they were merchants as well as landowners, with their own trading vessels sailing to England and the ports of northern Europe. By constant intermarriage these families judiciously kept their money and property within a tight-knit kinship network which controlled all social and political power in the county. The largest of these families was the Traills, who acquired estates on almost every island in Orkney.

George Traill from Blebo in Fife accompanied Earl Robert Stewart to Orkney. He purchased the estate of Quandale in Rousay, married a local heiress and established a dynasty. He may have been factor to Earl Patrick, but he survived the downfall of "Black Patie" and prospered with a lucrative money-lending business. Soon he had added the Westness estate in Rousay and one of the best houses in Kirkwall to his property. With his second wife, Isabel Craigie, George established further lines of Traills who in their turn married heiresses and acquired estates: Woodwick in Evie; Westness and Frotoft in Rousay; all the island of North Ronaldsay; Westove, Elsness and Hobbister on Sanday; Tirlet, Brough and Rapness in Westray and all Papay. The Traills of Holland were the senior branch of this powerful family who dominated local politics.

George's eldest son Thomas was one of many east coast Scots to seek their fortune in the Protestant armies engaged in the Thirty Years War. This conflict, which ravaged Europe between 1618 and 1648, seems to have provided lucrative opportunites for the Scots mercenaries. Thomas Traill served with the Swedish king Gustavus Adolphus who had 34 Scots colonels in his forces, 50 Scots lieutenant-colonels and at least one Orcadian major-general![4] Tradition credits Thomas with the talents of romantic poet as well as soldier, his songs including the first version of "My love is like a red, red rose", immortalised by Burns. If the tradition is true it sets Thomas in a much more attractive

George Traill, the sixth laird *(Orkney Museums Service)*

light than his immediate descendants, whose only quoted utterances are far from poetic! "Germany Thomas" retired to Orkney and in 1632 married his stepmother's sister (this was to become something of a family habit), Marion Craigie. On March 17, 1637 he bought "the house of Holland" from John Scollay of Manvel. Man(a)vel is the name of the field in front of the present house, a Georgian addition to substantial 17th-century buildings which almost certainly belonged to Scollay and suggest he owned a farm of some importance.

In addition to Holland Scollay sold "the 5½ penny udal land under his house of Hawkin and the 2½ penny udal land under his house of Leanig". As the whole island consisted of a total of 72 pennylands, Traill's first purchase was only a small portion, but this was just the beginning. Further entries in the Register of Sasines indicate that over the next 20 years Thomas Traill made several more purchases of udal land in Papay and Westray. In 1644 he bought more land "be-south the yard" in Papay; in 1649 another parcel of Howquin from its proprietor Marion Moneypenny; in 1655 lands in Aikerness and Brough in Westray and further lands in Papay and in Skaill in 1664.[5] As Holland expanded, other properties were gradually absorbed. The 14 udallers recorded in Papay in 1601 were reduced to six small lairds, besides Traill, in 1653[6] and early in the next century his grandson was sole owner of the island with all its "houses biggings yeards tofts crofts toumalls quoys quoylands outbreaks onsets anexis conexis parts pendicles et pertinents".[7] This pattern of the amalgamation of small freehold properties into large estates was happening all over Orkney at this time.

The original Holland House stood about a quarter of a mile from the present one, on the "Knowe of Old Holland". The only surviving traces of it are some of the carved oak panels from the dining-room, (now in the Orkney Museum in Kirkwall), which bear the initials of the first and second laird and their wives. Thomas was succeeded by his son George and grandson Thomas, and in all there were seven generations of Traills of Holland, Thomases and Georges alternating, who ruled the estate for the next two and a half centuries. Unfortunately, there is little recorded of the 18th-century Traills and only Thomas, the third laird, achieved immortality in local tradition. He is remembered for terrorising his tenantry with an appalling temper which frequently erupted into violence, and they credited him with dealing with the Devil, apparently on a fairly equal footing.

In the North Isles Presbytery Records the "Wicked Laird" makes frequent appearances before the Session, and seems indeed to have been a belligerent, grasping and vituperative individual, prone to apoplectic rages and unpleasant invective. For years the long-suffering minister and elders of the Kirk Session made heroic efforts to rebuke successive lairds of Holland, (George the second laird, son Thomas, grandsons George and Peter) for their repeated sins of fornication and Sabbath-breaking, and persuade them to "submit themselves to the Session" and mend their ways. The minister of Westray and Papay, the Reverend William Blaw (who had the misfortune to be Thomas Traill's brother-in-law) refused to baptise his child unless he promised the Session never to be guilty of Sabbath breach again, and Thomas "did accordingly promise, but ever since he hath carried on an implacable hatred to the Minister".[8]

Thomas Traill, the seventh laird. He is seated on the "Holland Chair" reputedly made from panelling from the Old Holland House and bearing the inscription *Com good folk and mak good chear al civil people ar welcome heir.*

(Orkney Library Photographic Archive)

For pages of Session minutes splattered with unecclesiastical epithets we read of Thomas refusing to pay his tiends (tithes), harassing the tenant of the minister's glebe, threatening the Kirk elders, smashing the furniture in the Kirk and stealing the poor-box, and attacking the minister in kirkyard and pulpit. The Reverend Blaw fared little better with Traill's sons. In 1718 the Session attempted to discipline Peter for sexual misdemeanours. He and his elder brother met Blaw in St Boniface kirkyard and "threatened him, using Dreadfull oaths and horrid Imprecations". In support of his sons, Thomas "came to the Church that day, as it would seem designedly, for he had not done so many years before", created a "Scandalous Riot" and beat the minister's boatmen with their own oars with frightful threats if they should attempt to land him on the isle again. From then on Blaw could only reach St Boniface Kirk by landing at the "minister's flag" two miles distant and walking along the foreshore. Unsurprisingly, he begged the Presbytery to relieve him of the obligation to travel to Papay.[9]

R. P. Fereday's description of the 18th-century Orkney lairds fits the Traills perfectly.

> "Though inclined to episcopalian and Jacobite sentiments, most lairds were much more interested in island politics and personal aggrandisement. They sought to extract as much rent and labour as they could from their tenants and farm servants. They were eager to swallow up the property of the remaining udallers or obtain lands from neighbouring lairds who were incapable or unfortunate. They strove to curb, subordinate and, eventually, exploit the authority of the Presbyterian ministers. Above all they hoped to reduce or evade the burden of scat payable to their feudal superiors".[10]

Thomas of Holland did all these things with enthusiasm. He considerably increased his tenants' rents and was ruthless in his demands for their labour. He twice had his goods impounded for failing to pay his superior duty or cess (land tax), and he absolutely detested Presbyterianism.

The episcopalian sentiments of the early 18th-century lairds had little to do with religion, let alone with an interest in bishops. They were an inherited accessory of the landowning class, most of whom probably felt, like Charles II, that "presbytery was not a religion for gentlemen". Blaw was by no means the only presbyterian minister in Orkney to have a hard time at the hands of the local laird. The Reverend Keith, minister in Hoy, complained that Lady Melsetter threatened him with her horsewhip and "sent to tell me. . . that she had four charged pistols prepared for me and any messenger that came firth to crave my stipend from her". [11]

The Traills of Holland were careful not to compromise themselves during the Jacobite rebellions, but there is little doubt that their sympathies did not lie with the Hanoverian succession or with presbyterian government. One day when the minister was at dinner at Holland, Thomas "cursed him to his face . . . and cried out before the whole Company he hoped to see him and all the government hanged as they were at Bodwell Brig and Pentland hills".[12] The reference would not have been lost on an Orcadian dinner party. After the defeat of the Covenanting army at the Battle of Bothwell Brig in Lanarkshire in 1679, 200 Covenanter prisoners, condemned to be transported to the American plantations, were drowned when their ship foundered in a storm off Deerness.

Thomas's reputation eclipsed that of his descendants. His son George does not appear in stormy scenes in the Session House, although in the (perhaps rather jaundiced) testimony of the minister, he was "as great ane Enemy to him and as great a Terror to the people of Papa as his Father".[13] The fourth laird was not one to risk his wealth and position for rash oppositions or adherences. When many of the Orkney lairds were defying the Earl of Morton over feu duties, we find George paying his duties and being rewarded by election, in 1745, to the Baron Roll of the freeholders of the Stewartry of Orkney. In other words, he was one of only six men in the whole county entitled to vote. In 1746 several of his relatives were incriminated for contacting Prince Charles Stewart ("Bonnie Prince Charlie") and promising support to the rebellion and four

The old wing of Holland may well have been part of the original farmhouse that Thomas Scollay sold to the first Thomas Traill in 1637. This picture, with George and Isabella Rendall of Cuppin on the cart, was taken in the 1960s.

lairds, John Traill of Elsness, John Traill of Westness, William Balfour of Trenaby and George's father-in-law Archibald Stewart of Brugh, spent months hiding in caves in Westray, their houses burnt and their property looted or confiscated. George's wife sent the fugitives half a pound of tea. Holland remained above suspicion and continued to prosper. [14]

George and his son Thomas appear in the records of the Sheriff Court in 1769 when James Stewart of Brugh raised a petition against his brothers-in-law.[15] (Father and son were both married to sisters of James at that time, which perhaps overstrained the in-law relationship). According to Stewart, the Traills were stealing his peats in Skelwick in Westray and attacking his servants when they tried to gather them. As Papay has no peat of its own and supplies had to be brought from Westray (where it was running out) or Eday, it can be imagined that peat-rights were aggressively defended. Traill in turn accused Stewart of "most atrocious riot and breach of the peace" in attacking *his* tenants when peat-gathering. It is hard to avoid the impression that they were not an agreeable family.

18th-century Orkney lairds were merchants first and foremost, shipping the produce of their island estates across the North Sea in return for essentials such as timber, tar and ploughs. A list of Orkney's exports for the year 1693 is a succinct summary of her economy. "The Chief Products of this Countrey, and which are exported yearly be the Merchant are Bear, Malt, Fish, Tallow, Hyds, Stockines, Butter, Selch-skines (seal-skins), Otter-skines, Rabbet-skines, Lamb skines, White-salt, Stuffs, Writing-Pens (goose quills), Downs, Feathers, Hams, Wool Etc".[16] In the course of the next century trade in both directions expanded. Orkney's produce was still primarily fish and agricultural goods but kelp and linen cloth had become important exports by the late 18th century, and the list of imports had grown considerably.[17] Among the timber, cartwheels and hardware are coals, an interesting addition in view of the squabbles over the Skelwick Moss, and the quantity of luxury goods suggests that Orkney society was not altogether unconvivial. For lairds like the Traills, port wine, sherry, rum, brandy, gin, snuff, tea, tobacco and gingerbread were among the pre-requisites of the good life, and undoubtedly found their way to the Holland tables.

Thomas, the fifth laird of Holland, was one of the merchant lairds much oppressed by the extremely high import duties on such commodities as spirits, spices and the decadent new luxury, tea. Having their own sloops engaged in legitimate trade with the Continent, they were in an ideal position to rectify the inconvenience by doing a little additional trading in duty-free goods. When the Orkney sloop *Peggy* left Rotterdam in 1770 she was laden with a cargo of spirits, cinnamon water, 90 lbs of black tea, tobacco stalks, 144 packs of playing cards and 31 cotton handkerchiefs, most of which was intended for secret unloading in Westray and Papay. "Young Holland was kind enough to offer all the assistance in his power, has promised the use of his fish house here and other houses, that it may be disposed of in the most convenient and safest manner. . . the whole affair may be managed with less noise in Papay then here (Westray), and lies in a more convenient spot to be secreted and concealed". Unfortunately this particular consignment never made it to the secrecy of Papay. The *Peggy* was arrested in a fog in the North Sea, with fake bills of lading made out for Bergen.[18]

There were much less glamorous ways in which lairds like Thomas could turn an honest penny. If the agriculture of the time was so inefficient that their farms could only afford a small surplus of grain for export (in years of good harvest), their island estates were well endowed with natural resources. The "rabbet-skines" and feathers mentioned in the list of exports above were both important items in the Papay economy. "The south end of the Island abounds with Rabbits", declared George Low,[19] "which are much valued for their flesh and skins". (Rabbits were certainly serious business - in 1792 there were 36,000 rabbit skins shipped from Stromness.)[20] There were also the huge flocks of sea-birds which nested every year on the cliffs of Westray and Papay and on the Holm, providing Traill with both gulls' eggs and young gulls. Auks were captured in great numbers for their feathers by being "swapped" on the cliffs or driven into large nets suspended across the geo where they were nesting. "Mr Traill caught upwards of seventy scores of auks in a single goe (*sic*) in one day, in the island of Papay Westray. . . and Mr Logie, merchant in the island of Westray, gave him £9 18s sterling for the feathers of birds. . ." [21]

Thomas was succeeded by his son George, the sixth laird, who became a Burgess of Kirkwall in 1808, and a Justice of the Peace. At home in Papay he was known as the Parish Bull. George made his mark on island history by fathering a great number of illegitimate children during his long and cheerful bachelorhood. To do him credit, all his children were acknowledged and provided for, and their mothers rewarded with annuities and farms. With unconscious irony Patrick Neill painted a genial picture of George, residing "in the midst of many contented, though poor, cottars, whose happiness we believe it is his study to promote, and with whom he mingles with the most perfect familiarity". [22] He fathered another eight children with his wife Mary Swan and died at the age of 66 in 1840.

Aberdeen Angus cows in front of Holland House, built by George Traill in 1814.

George could afford to be cheerful and generous. His annual land rents of £1641 4s 0d set him in the top bracket of Orkney landholders and he entered his inheritance when the boom in kelp prices was starting to bring enormous profits to Orkney lairds, especially those with island estates whose coastlines provided great quantities of seaweed. According to *The Statistical Account*, Papay was producing 70 tons of kelp annually, or more per capita of population than any other island, and this was a harvest that, however hard-won by the labourers, cost the laird only a trifling investment in a few simple tools. Like most of his contemporaries, George enjoyed spending his easy-come fortune on conspicuous consumption in Kirkwall and invested little in his estates apart from building larger and more fashionable new houses. An imposing mansion was built at Brough on Westray and around 1810 "Old Holland" was demolished and a new Orkney-Georgian Holland House built in Papay.

The price of kelp, the product of burning sea-ware and an essential source of alkali for the glass- and soap-making industries, had been kept high by the Napoleonic Wars which prevented the import of cheaper alternatives. When trade resumed with the Continent, Spanish barilla undercut British kelp and as import duties were lowered and finally abolished in the 1820s the price of kelp fell. Deprived of their income,

Orkney lairds at last considered paying some attention to the cultivation of their estates. "Farmer George" - as his family knew him - was one of the first lairds to change direction and take serious steps to improve the agricultural potential of his land through enclosure and reclamation.

Thomas, the seventh laird, reached the age of 21 in 1843 and inherited the estate at exactly the moment when radical agricultural change became possible, and extremely profitable. "A keen improver of the land and a first rate farmer",[23] he immediately launched into an enthusiastic programme of enclosure, drainage, liming, building, and the introduction of the latest ideas on crop and livestock husbandry. Labour was plentiful and cheap, and cattle and sheep prices soared. It was a golden age of new ideas, new inventions and hitherto undreamt-of profits. Thomas Traill was one of the foremost pioneers of the new farming, and Holland and Brough became model farms, much admired by contemporaries.

However, in 1886 he was declared bankrupt. The meteoric price rises of the 1850s and 1860s slumped in the 1870s in a recession that seriously affected the whole country, but it seems unlikely that even the most astronomic income could have kept Thomas afloat. Despite his initial enthusiasm for farming, he increasingly spent time away from Papay leaving his estates in the hands of his farm managers and leading a life that no agricultural estate could ever have supported. As early as 1867 he was giving a Bond for £13,000 on the security of the estate,[24] (a sum that would have paid the annual wages of one of his farm-servants a thousand times over!)

Perhaps the instincts of his merchant laird ancestry reasserted themselves, but whether it was through disastrous business ventures or (as tradition hints) gambling, or simply high living, Thomas ran up debts to the staggering sum of £32,000, far more than his entire estate was worth. (In 1881 the value of all the buildings he owned on Papay and Westray was estimated for insurance purposes: the mansion houses at Holland, worth £1200, and Brough, £600, and their large steadings, the grieves' houses, farm cottages and kelp stores, the houses and shops in Broughton village, the farms of Gallowhill and Clifton, the meal mills and threshing mills all totalled under £10,000). In 1880 a bond was registered securing all Traill's lands in Papay and Westray to William Baird of Elie, his principal creditor.[25] In 1886 the estate was sequestered and taken over by the creditors' Trustees.[26]

It was the end of the 250 year era in which the Traill family had owned Holland and dominated the island. Besides his family home, Thomas Traill had a lot to lose. At the time of his bankruptcy he was the ninth largest proprietor in Orkney, and owner of 5,780 acres. Some of the land was sold off in small parcels by the Trustees, other lands were requisitioned by the Crofters' Commission to enlarge tenants' holdings; the diminished estate continued to be managed by the Trustees and did not disintegrate altogether until they sold it in 1922.

***

III

A Wretched State of Agriculture

Our agriculture is a constant endeavour to avoid a loss, in which we are not animated by any expectation of positive profit.
Thomas Balfour 1795

Although Thomas Traill's bankruptcy eventually lost him the estate, it was his enthusiastic investment in the 1850s and 1860s which radically modernised the farm and in fact transformed the whole island. It was due to the efforts of "Improving Lairds" like Thomas that Orkney farms were able to cram their evolution from medieval to modern times into a couple of hectic decades. The extent of this achievement can only be appreciated by realising just how backward Orkney's agriculture was until the mid 19th century in comparison to the rest of the country.

The "agricultural revolution" came to Scotland as a whole much more slowly than England, but rapid progress was made in the course of the late 18th century and the first decades of the 19th century. At the end of that time farming north of the border, at least in the more favoured areas like the Lothians, was often more advanced than in the south. Agricultural production was stimulated by the demand for food to feed a growing urban population, and made possible by the new knowledge of agricultural science. There were new theories concerning the rotation of crops, the sowing of turnips for winter keep and of artificial grasses, the enclosure and drainage and liming of fields, the introduction of improved strains of grain and breeds of livestock, and every other aspect of farming. As these ideas were put into practice farm output and profitability increased and the value of agricultural estates, even in the Highlands, soared. Scottish gentry had founded the "Honourable Society of Improvers in the Knowledge of Agriculture in Scotland" in 1723 and husbandry and "Improvements" became the fashionable pursuit of the 18th-century proprietor.

The fashion spread only slowly to the Orkney lairds. They were merchants who made their incomes from commerce and, until the kelp boom years, looked to their island estates only for a rent paid in the traditional grain crops which they could trade and the prestige that went with land ownership. The grain-trade was a high-risk business: in years of bad harvest the tenants could not pay their rents and there was little to sell, in good years grain was plentiful and so prices were low, and sometimes the cargo was spoiled during delayed journeys. However, despite the losses, the trade must have been lucrative enough to bring prosperity to lairds like the Traills.[1]

There is an excellent description of agriculture in Westray and Papay in 1793 written by the local minister, the Reverend James Izat, for *The Statistical Account* and at that time farming had changed so little from its medieval state that this account could serve for the previous several centuries. The only significant innovation that Izat mentions is the introduction of the potato, which was first cultivated in Orkney around 1750.

"Agriculture in this parish is carried on in the same way that it has been done for many years past. The field are all open, without inclosures, neither are there any green crops raised here, such as hay, turnips etc; the people here now begin to plant potatoes. . . . The farmer here generally uses a plough with one stilt, much in the form of the old Roman plough. The only rotation of crops is small grey oats and bear; the time of sowing the oats is in the month of March. . . The only manure here is sea-weed, with the help of what house-dung they can produce. This they lay on the fields which produced oats the preceding season, and this is done immediately after harvest, and during the winter, as often as the wind and tides bring this manure ashore. In the spring season, after the oats are sown, the farmer gives the wared land one ploughing, which they call their fallow. . . The farmer gives the bear land one ploughing only after the fallow, at the time he sows the seed. . ."[2]

Izat's account is corroborated by the meticulous diary kept by Patrick Fea of Stove in Sanday throughout the last three decades of the 18th century. Through his terse but precise entries emerges a vivid picture of the farming routine on a large North Isles farm, or in fact anywhere in Orkney. The year revolves around the cultivation of the land and the arduous preparation of the grain for milling. All through the winter "his people" are busy in the barn, threshing the oats and bere, winnowing the grain and drying it in the kiln, cleaning it ready for grinding in the mill, or preparing seed for sowing next year's crop. Whenever the weather allows, they are gathering seaweed from the shore and spreading it upon the land ready for ploughing, which will start in February or March. The sowing of oats in March is followed by spreading ware and ploughing the bere ground, sown in May. In June and July farmwork slackens as the season for kelp begins, and this will occupy all the available labour until the time of mowing the hay crop in August. In September is the harvest and, except in a very bad season, the last sheaves are led to the stackyard by mid October. Lifting tatties continues all October. In November, the workhorses are in their stables and a few cattle are killed and salted; the remainder will scavenge for a meagre living on the arable ground all winter.[3]

It was a world in which enclosure, drainage, rotation of crops, the selective breeding of livestock or the growing of winter keep were unknown. Visitors who had seen all these things gradually transforming the landscape and economy of mainland Scotland were astonished to find Orkney almost untouched by the new science or by any desire among its lairds to improve the miserable unproductivity of their lands or the poverty of the tenants and labourers who worked them.

Beneath Orkney's thin upper crust of proprietors and large tenants were the ranks of the "peerie tenants", who held their scattered rigs of arable ground without any security of tenure and out of their scanty crops had to pay not only rents to the landlord but teinds to the minister. Below them were the cottars, who held a house and a small piece of cultivated land called a harvest-fee in return for being bound to work in the landlord's fields or on his kelp-shores. He might also rent one or two coogills of grassland (one coogill = a cow's grazing for the summer), for which he paid in butter and fowls, and he had the right to keep a sheep or two on the common pasture, paying the laird a tenth of their wool and produce. He was also expected to pay in a multiplicity of ill-defined services.[4]

When he was giving his evidence to the Crofters Commission in 1888, Thomas Traill's solicitor Mr Drever claimed that the proprietor had abolished most of his tenants' labour services and payments in kind for a money rent. "Prior to his time there had been practically no money passing in the island of Papa. The rents had all been paid in kind".[5] This had been the situation all over Orkney ever since powerful families such as the Traills had started to devour the property of the small freeholders and reduce them to tenant status. Their position was precarious. Leases were invariably short, for three years or even as little as a year at a time, and payments known as grassums had to be made at each renewal of a lease. If this was not discouraging enough, the tenant was hindered with the burden of "onca" services (literally "on call"), which inevitably obliged him to work in the laird's fields at exactly the time when his own crops demanded attention.

Under an autocratic laird the tenant could be little more than an unpaid labourer. In 1718 the North Isles Presbytery heard how "Thomas Traill of Holland, casting off all fear of God and regard to man . . . also does most wickedly prophane the Sabbath by calling his Servants to his house upon the same and then and there contriving and commanding all the work that is to be done all the week after, and when Sermon falls at Papa causing ane officer cry at the Church door that the People come to work upon Monday with their pleughs, harrows, creeills and barrows . . . "[6] Tenants were much more burdened by obligations of labour service in Orkney than in other areas, and remained so until well into the 19th century. William Thomson draws a revealing parallel between the payments in kind and labour services made by a 9th-century villein on a French manor and by an Orcadian tenant farmer in 1834. The latter was technically free to leave his estate if he wished, but otherwise the closeness of the similarity is astonishing.[7]

As agriculture stagnated in its medieval state, so did the standard of living of the ordinary people. While considerable luxury and sophistication were found in the lairds' houses in the 18th century, the homes of their small tenants could not be said to have advanced in material comfort since the time of the Knap of Howar. "Their houses are very simply builded with pebble stone, without any chimneys, the fire being made in the midst thereof. The good man, wife, children and other of their family eat and sleep on the one side of the house, and the cattle on the other, very beastly and rudely, in respect of civility".[8] Martin Frobisher's description of Orkney in 1577 (which represents living conditions all over the Highlands and Islands) held good for almost another 300 years. Walter Traill Dennison remembered the houses in Sanday in the mid 19th century as single room hovels built mostly of turf, without windows and with only a straw mat for a door, and almost without furniture. (In one house a family of eight slept in one bed 5ft 8in by 3ft 10in in size – Dennison measured it in his astonishment!)[9]

Visitors found Orkney houses "miserable-looking abodes . . . the door, which is in many cases common to the cot and the cow-house, is sometimes less than five feet high - the cows turning into one end of the building and the people to the other; and often a favourite or delicate cow, or a few calves, are kept in the fire-house or but, along with the family."[10] There was no possibility that the tenant would invest materials or effort into improving his home or his fields while he had no security of possessing them beyond the next rent day.

Some 18th-century writers such as the Reverend Thomas Hepburn of Birsay or James Fea lambasted the lairds for perpetuating a system of tenure which ensured bad husbandry as well as a wretched poverty. "The flourishing state of agriculture in England is much owing to the humanity of the landlords; most part of our Orkney lairds seem to be absolutely devoid of this divine principle; they crush the spirit of improvement in the farmers, by short leases, grassums, numerous unlimited services, and many other hardships".[11]

Hepburn and Fea represented a growing tide of frustration within Orkney at the backwardness of the county. As early as 1757 Hepburn had written a scathing attack on the lairds' refusal to modernise their estates. "The state of agriculture is very rude in all these isles . . . their plow has but one stilt, the plow-irons are so clumsy and short, that the furrow is very shallow and unequal, and must often be delved with spades; their harrow is small, light and timber-teethed; they use no wheel-carriages, nor oxen plows, though their horses are but of the ordinary shelty kind; they never fallow their corn lands . . . How rude must agriculture be in that country, where they winnow all their corns through their fingers, instead of sieves, riddles, or fanners? What sort of farmers must they be, who fleece fine meadow grounds, to lay on their corn lands? What judgement will you form of one of their principal heritors, who being told that this practice turned all his fine meadows into lakes and marshes, replied 'That he cared not if they carried all the ground to one ridge, provided they paid him his rent'".[12]

According to John Firth, whose *"Reminiscences of an Orkney Parish"* recorded the customs of the latter half of the 19th century, the method of winnowing with the hands was still common in Orkney 100 years later.[13] The "fleecing" of meadow grounds refers to the practice of removing turf from the common grazing to use as manure on the arable ground. It is no wonder that visiting farmers were scandalised!

Hepburn's criticisms of the disastrous methods of agriculture were probably accurate, (he was the son of an East Lothian farmer), but as a minister he was dependent for his living on his patron Lord Morton, so he fails to mention the role that this man played in perpetuating this depressing state of affairs. The Earls of Morton held the Earldom of Orkney from the time of Charles I until 1766 when the 14th Earl sold the estate to the enormously wealthy arms-dealer and entrepreneur Sir Lawrence Dundas. Morton and his successor Dundas had a complete stranglehold on the Orkney economy and agriculture was crippled by the appalling burden of Crown rents and feu-duties which had to be paid to them annually in oatmeal, malt and bere. In years of poor harvest it was impossible for the tenant to grow enough to pay the rents and feed his family, and these happened frequently in the cycles of exceptionally severe weather that occurred during the 17th and 18th centuries.

The terrible winters and cold wet summers that devastated crops and killed animals in their thousands in the 1690s were long remembered as "King William's Years". A century later, a "Memorial for the Heritors" states that "horses, cattle and sheep are daily perishing in numbers for want"[14] in the long and bitter winter that followed the fourth harvest to fail almost completely in seven years. In Orkney (as in the more famous Irish potato famine of 1846), grain was being collected as rent and shipped out of the country while people were literally dropping dead in the fields from hunger.

When grain was non-existent, Dundas' rent-collectors demanded its money value at famine prices. "In other parts of Scotland the distresses of the year 1783 have inclined humane proprietors to abate their rents. In Orkney alone the exactions increase with the inability of the inhabitants to pay".

The necessity to pay feu duties in grain also made it impossible for anyone to change direction in agriculture, even when they wanted to do so. As James Fea pointed out in 1775, "by this means we are obliged to give our attention more to the raising of Bear than to the cultivation of other kinds of more useful grain, or to the raising of black Cattle, which ought to be our principal object".[15] Other landowners, such as Thomas Balfour of Shapinsay, were also well aware that the land and climate were far more suitable for livestock rearing than growing grain. As Balfour bitterly told Sir John Sinclair: "a legal title is given to exact from the tenants and proprietors of these Islands, a quantity of grain, which it is always difficult, often impossible for them to deliver. . . accordingly, we are maintaining a struggle with nature, with climate and situation, as constant as it is unprofitable, for the production of grain, to the exclusion of those crops and modes of agriculture, to which our climate, situation, and soil, are so happily adapted".[16]

Balfour, admittedly, had an axe to grind as he was a political opponent of Dundas, but the cumbersome and antiquated system of payments certainly hindered progress. In 1814 John Shirreff, Reporter to the Board of Agriculture, was horrified to find Orkney impoverished by a rental in kind which would be "an oppressive burden upon the agriculture of a district of far superior value". Feu duties amounted to 5,000 bolls of grain, 2,680 stones of butter and 700 English gallons of oil; burdens which "collected . . . from the poorest, and at least one of the worst cultivated countries in Scotland, were ruinous to the highest degree".[17]

Despite these discouragements, there had been attempts to introduce modern farming practices even early in the 18th century. James Moodie of Melsetter and Sir James Stewart of Burray experimented with enclosures on their estates. After Stewart's imprisonment for supporting the Jacobite cause and death in Southwark Jail in 1746, an inventory of his possessions was made in 1747 which included an astonishing number of very up to date agricultural implements, even a turnip drill plough long before turnips were grown as a field crop in Lowland Scotland. Most of the implements are described as broken, however, so perhaps the new-fangled inventions did not find favour with Stewart's labourers! (The "turneep drill plew" was found in the Long Gallery amongst many other agricultural implements, chests of fine linen, 9 oxen yoaks and 65 bowes for oxen, 9 lbs of wigg peuder, a seal net, a speaking trumpet, 4 Gulf clubs, 2 whereof broken, ane old armour . . .).[18]

In 1784 Colonel Thomas Balfour purchased the estate of Sound in Shapinsay. Here he experimented with enclosing his land and reclaiming the common, resettling his cottars and introducing turnips, but most of such attempts were piecemeal and there was still no fundamental change to the traditional system of arable farming. The first really thorough "improvements" were made at Graemeshall in the parish of Holm in 1828 when John Irving and the factor David Petrie, who ran the estate for absentee laird Alexander Sutherland Graeme, cleared away the runrig and divided the land into compact farms.

Early attempts at improvement were not, of course, appreciated. Malcolm Laing started to drain and enclose his lands at Stove in Sanday "and was abundantly cursed for doing so." A modernising tenant in Stronsay had his new implements flung over the crags, and "so determined was the opposition he met with from the people that the farmer had to give up. And the farm of Housbie, now the finest in the country, had to lie for forty years more in its primitive and wilderness state."[19]

By the time that the *New Statistical Account* was written in 1841 most of Orkney was still lagging far behind other parts of the country. Much of the arable land was still held in runrig, each tenant cultivating his irregular plots which were grazed by the livestock of the whole township all winter. Lacking any artificial drainage or fertiliser, the soil was waterlogged and the yields from the unvaried crops of oats and bere very low. The common land was ruined for grazing by being stripped of turf for manure and fuel. There were no roads, and so hardly any wheeled transport, in the county. The livestock were half-starved for lack of winter feeding and very small. "In Orkney, agriculture is generally in the most wretched state" wrote John Dickson in the *Highland and Agricultural Society Transactions* of 1841, "perhaps no part of the kingdom can exhibit it in a worst condition, or where naturally good soil is more abused."[20]

Dickson's outsider judgement is perhaps harsh. Orkney lairds could experiment with the new husbandry but they could not overcome geography. The Pentland Firth put a hopeless barrier between the Northern Isles and the expanding markets of the south. Salted beef, the "flesche" collected as rent, had been regularly exported to Leith but it was impossible to turn livestock rearing into profit while it was so impractical to export live animals in any number by sailing vessel. To change estates from the old system of crop production to an entirely different system of livestock husbandry required considerable capital investment and, until roads and steamships made the export of agricultural produce economic, there was no financial return for capital outlay. Most of the early "Improvers" were in fact ruined by their investment. Malcolm Laing's profits for a year on his newly-enclosed farm at Stove in Sanday were said to be 5d, and in succeeding years the estate ran at "heavy and increasing loss".[21]

A Kirkwall society founded in 1826 was one of several doomed attempts at "promoting improvements in husbandry". In 1841 the Orkney Agricultural Society got off to a shaky start. Its annual report in 1844 concluded that "the paralysis which came over agricultural enterprise in Orkney about the year 1830" was caused by the almost total loss of the revenue from kelp and the very low prices for grain and livestock "causing the decline of profit and continued exhaustion of means which made Landlords . . . fearful of increasing burdens already too large by outlay in farming improvements".[22]

Besides, Orkney lairds had no tradition of investing capital in farming. The fortunes so quickly made during the kelp boom years were squandered again as quickly, and had a serious effect on Orkney's development. In *The Statistical Account* the Reverend James Izat correctly prophesied that "it may be depended on as a certain fact, that agriculture will only be a secondary consideration in this county while kelp continues to sell at any tolerable price."[23] Elsewhere in Scotland, land was rapidly becoming more productive as modern farming methods were adopted, but in Orkney production actually fell. Crops, especially the modern ones such as turnips which required intensive cultivation in the early summer, competed with kelp work and as long as kelp was profitable there was no incentive for lairds to divert their labour force into agriculture. Both farming and fishing were disastrously neglected in the islands during the late 18th and early 19th centuries.

In the 1820s kelp prices slumped and they crashed in 1830, fulfilling Patrick Neill's prophecy of 1806: "should the market for kelp . . . unexpectedly fail, the landholders of Orkney will find, when too late, the great imprudence of thus neglecting the cultivation and improvement of their land."[24] These were difficult years but, luckily for the landowners, the first steamship service to Orkney was introduced in 1833 and within a few years a new way of making an income from their estates would become possible: the export of livestock. By the 1840s the steamships connecting Orkney with the markets in Aberdeen and Leith were sufficiently large and fast to carry regular consignments of live cattle, and farming finally became worthy of attention.

Once the process had begun, the speed with which Orkney's agriculture was modernised is amazing. In the space of about 25 years from the late 1840s Orkney landowners transformed their estates. Fields were enclosed and drained, waste land reclaimed, new crops, new machinery, new techniques of cultivation and new breeds of livestock introduced. The value of agricultural exports and farm profits soared. In the period between 1833 and 1870 the value of cattle and horses exported from Orkney rose from £5,450 to £85,000, and the acreage of land in cultivation from 25,000 to 70,000 acres.[25] George and Thomas Traill (the sixth and seventh lairds) were amongst the foremost landlords in bringing the "agricultural revolution" to the islands, a revolution that transformed the landscape of Orkney and the lives of the people living here.

The Kelp Stores *(Inga Hourston)*

IV

The Golden Age

Landscape plotted and pieced - fold, fallow and plough.
Gerard Manley Hopkins, "Pied Beauty"

Until the 19th century Papay must have looked much as it had done for centuries past, but in the space of a few decades it was changed irrevocably. It is necessary to try to imagine the island as it was around 1800: entirely without the stone dykes that seem such a characteristic part of the landscape today; all the land open, the irregular rigs of arable land divided only by the baulks made by the plough; water lying on the undrained fields and the moorland of the North Hill extending much further than at present; the scattering of low, windowless turf-roofed houses hardly distinguishable from the landscape.

It is possible that the very first enclosures on Papay were made at quite an early date by George Traill (1773-1840) or his father Thomas (1728-1813). Shirreff reports that "there were a couple of brood mares, of the draught sort in the inclosures *(sic)* of Papa Westray in September 1808".[1] However, Shirreff's further comments reveal that kelp, rather than farming, was still the principal interest at Holland. "Old Mr Traill . . . had always about a score of horses of one kind and another, many or almost all employed, in summer, in carrying seaweed to be manufactured into kelp, or remaining idle in that season, as no turnip are raised in Papa Westray, and the peat used for fuel is all brought in large open boats from other islands, chiefly from the neighbouring island of Westray".

It was probably in the 1830s that George Traill undertook the first serious schemes of enclosure and reclamation on his estates, which included Brough and Rapness in Westray as well as the whole island of Papay.[2] Papay must have been a particularly attractive proposition for pioneering improving ideas; it was small and "deemed among the most fertile of the islands in Orkney."[3] The Westray estates perhaps posed more of a problem. A large part of the island was hill and moorland, and Rapness was almost cut off by impassable bog in the winter. According to both *The Statistical Account* and the *New Statistical Account*, the land and livestock was poorer than in Papay. "The larger cows do not take well with the bare pastures of Westray. . . owing to the backward state of agriculture. In Papay, where the pastures are better, the larger breed of cattle and horses do pretty well".[4]

There is little evidence in the *New Statistical Account* that George Traill and the other proprietors attempted to introduce improvements to Westray. By the time the minister of Westray and Papay wrote his report in 1839 many Orkney parishes had divided their hill land, the commonty, where all the livestock grazed together in the summer months, but the interior of Westray still consisted of "an immense tract of common hill and dale lying in a state of nature, and separated everywhere from the cultivated lands by a turf dike, within which all the flocks and most of the bestial of the

The steading from the north, with barns, grain lofts and the circular mill tramp
(Inga Hourston)

island . . . are shut . . . until the crops are removed from the ground . . . when the styles are again laid open and the flocks left to range at pleasure."[5] It was a system that made improvement of crops or livestock impossible.

On Papay, on the other hand, George Traill was setting seriously about the business of being an "improving laird". "A large proportion of this island is under culture, and enclosed with stone dikes" reported the Reverend Armit approvingly, and "Mr Traill adds every year to his cultivated property in Papa, by allowing his people to enclose what they can, of the waste or uncultivated, and to enjoy what is thus gained rent free, for the space of seven years". He also experimented with some of the new crops, and apparently with great success. "Here clover, white and red, grows spontaneously, and of a rich quality. Here turnips are raised, of a more extraordinary size and weight than in warmer climes and apparently richer soils". [6]

George even became so enthusiastic about growing things that he succumbed to the fashion for building a large walled kitchen garden where, if his blackcurrants and gooseberries were a little disappointing, his espaliered apple trees were "wonderfully productive".[7] It would be surprising if there had not been a vegetable garden at Holland before this, however, for 18th-century Orcadians were far more enthusiastic about vegetables than their descendants. At Stove in Sanday Patrick Fea grew cabbages, curly kale, leeks, onions, carrots, spinach, parsnips, beetroot, lettuce and radishes as well as potatoes, and it can be assumed that a similar range of produce would have been found on the dinner table at Holland.

Nothing that George introduced could have made a greater difference to his labourers than the horse-driven threshing mill, which was installed at Holland by 1823[8] and replaced the remorseless winter task of threshing the crop by flail. The fact that this machine was one of the first of its kind to be seen in Orkney, and erected some years before the kelp crash, is more evidence that George was taking a serious interest in his farm before most of his fellow lairds. The fine north range of the steading, with the two-storey threshing barn and long grain lofts running above the haybarn and stables, appear on an estate plan of 1844, only a few years after George's death, so it is likely that they were at least planned by him.

George certainly "improved" Holland considerably in his lifetime, but there were still no fundamental changes in the traditional system, and he did not live to see farming bring a new era of prosperity to Orkney landlords. Enclosure and the introduction of turnips and sown grasses was still only happening piecemeal; on most of the arable land bere and oats were still cropped in constant succession, and there was little artificial drainage. Money was almost unknown in a cumbersome farm economy based on a rental paid in services, kelp, poultry, and the notoriously unpleasant concoction known as Orkney butter, which was, wrote James Fea, "sold for laying sheep, and greasing Coach wheels, to the everlasting disgrace of our country".[9]

George Traill died in 1840; his eldest son Thomas was not yet 21 and enthusiastic to grasp the exciting new opportunities for experiment and innovation on an agricultural estate. In 1833 the first steamship service between Kirkwall and Leith had been inaugurated, and as it rapidly improved livestock exports at last became profitable. Aberdeenshire cattle dealers started trading in Orkney and from the late 1840s the price of cattle rose steeply. It was not until 1865 that the "Elegant, Commodious and Fast Screw Steamship Orcadia, Built and Fitted especially for the Trade, and carrying Her Majesty's Mails" started twice-weekly sailings ("unless prevented by any unforeseen occurrence") round the North Isles,[10] but there must have been cattle-boats before this to take the isles' beasts to Kirkwall, for the rising prices are certainly evident in Traill's farm accounts. Landowners could also take advantage of public money made available for the improvement of farmland and transport. In 1846 Peel's government passed the Public Money Drainage Act which offered loans to landlords for land drainage schemes. Another Drainage Act followed in 1849 and in 1857 the Orkney Roads Act made money available for constructing roads in the county. Agricultural investment suddenly became both fashionable and financially rewarding.

Thomas immediately launched into an enthusiastic programme of "Improvement" on his estates. Modern husbandry demanded enclosure as a pre-requisite of scientific farming, and in 1844 he had a map drawn up of Papay with the entire island "squared" and the acreages of each new field meticulously noted. Soon afterwards Brough was divided into a regular grid of 20 acre fields, and in 1848 the surveyors descended on his 2,600 acre property in Rapness. The home farms were laid out in regular fields and each small tenant farm was given a consolidated plot of land. Houses that were inconveniently situated (or, like Bolispel, may have blotted the view from the mansion house) were removed.

In retrospect it is fortunate that not all of Traill's schemes went unopposed. The North Hill, (now an SSSI), is "squared" on the 1844 map and evidently he intended to bring the whole area under the plough. He was thwarted by the combination of his tenants, who bitterly resented losing their common grazing, his grieve and (according to J D Mackay), the Hillyans, the small people of the Hill who disliked disturbance and could cause great trouble if annoyed. John Mackay, Traill's manager and a sensible Caithness man who could see a non-starter for what it was, gave orders that as many plough-socks as possible were to be broken on the boulders. Probably neither the order nor fear of the Hillyans was necessary to encourage non-cooperation, but Traill was forced to leave most of the Hill in peace.[11]

The Holland rent books testify to the huge amount of labour that went into "Improvements". Tenants who were skilled dyke builders earned much of their rent in the late 1840s and 1850s by enclosing Holland's fields - at the rate of four pence or five pence a fathom. David Miller of Midhouse built 258 fathoms of dyke in 1847, 70½ fathoms in 1848 and 178 fathoms in 1849; David Groat of Quoys built 146 fathoms in 1847 and a further 178 fathoms of dyke on the Hill in 1851. Then there were the payments for quarrying and carting stones, for draining fields and carting dung or lime. In a typical entry for 1849, Thomas Miller of Nouster is credited with £1 15s 0d for carting stones, and 1s 0d a day for 16 days work draining Quavil and 10 days working in the quarry. Building roads and dykes carried on steadily into the 1870s. In 1869 George Miller was paid 9d a fathom for building 50½ fathoms of dyke, (approximately 100 metres). Four years later the rate has gone up to 1s 4d a fathom for his work at Burland.[12]

Gradually the open landscape of winding waterlogged rigs was replaced by square fields bounded by stone dykes, and these still clearly define the original extent of Holland. An elaborate grid of drainage ditches was dug even on the Holm. The introduction of a proper system of drains meant that the old hump-backed rigs were no longer necessary to throw off surface water, so the new fields could also be levelled to suit modern techniques of cultivation.

Traill's investment was stimulated by the soaring prices which his cattle were fetching. In 1850 store cattle were worth £3 to £6. The price climbed through the 1850s and 1860s and in 1867 his cattle were bought by an Aberdeenshire dealer for an average price of about £15. In 1871 his young beasts were selling for around £15 to £18, and fat beasts for over £20. Lambs that were worth 2s or 3s in 1841 were fetching 10 or 15 times that amount in 1871.[13] The main reasons for the amazing boom in prices were the improvement in communications and the huge demand for produce to feed the growing industrial population. Victorian Britain also maintained a regular army and a large navy which required victualling. Transport had to develop in speed and efficiency to keep pace with the demand for food. By the early 1870s "two powerful steamers" were plying weekly between Kirkwall and Granton near Edinburgh, and livestock could be shipped south, even from the North Isles, with relative ease. (As nowadays, things occasionally went wrong. In 1870 Traill's accounts noted receipt of £1 8s 6d, "the price of sheep lost between Kirkwall and Granton by the Shipping Company").[14]

At that time, however, prices peaked and levelled off, and in the mid 1880s fell significantly as the result of the huge increase in imported meat. The improvement in transport which had served Orkney so well was now serving to flood Britain with cheap food, brought by railroad and steamship from every part of the world. Wheat, grown on the huge and newly-mechanised prairie lands of the Americas, could be imported so cheaply that it totally undercut British grain and more than half the acreage of wheat in the country fell out of production. By the 1880s refrigerated steamships were bringing thousands of tons of beef from North America, Argentina, Australia and New Zealand.[15] The boom years were over and British farmers suffered a recession. However, cereal-growers were far worse hit than livestock producers who could at least benefit from cheap feedstuffs as the result of the low grain prices. The imported meat competed with the lower grades of British beef and mutton, but there was still a demand for high-quality meat, such as prime Aberdeen Angus beef from north-east Scotland.[16] In 1885 Traill could still obtain £16 for a good stot, which was more than most of his employees could earn in a year.

While farming was bringing in handsome profits, Traill could afford lavish expenditure on new buildings for his principal farms. Not only was the Holland steading enlarged but another large steading with a roofed mill tramp was built at Clifton in Westray, and Robert Pringle's prize-winning essay for the Highland and Agricultural Society praised "the fine farm of Brough" where "a commodious farm-steading has recently been added to meet the requirements of modern agriculture. . . the management is in accordance with the most advanced Scotch farming of the day".[17] While a wing of the Holland steading has been rebuilt in the late 20th century, the splendid steading at Brough survives virtually unaltered and illustrates the lay-out of the "model farm" of the 1860s, with barns, byres and stables forming a three-sided court around the midden.

The huge middens that characterise 19th-century steadings were a major innovation. Cattle, instead of wandering all over the arable ground in the winter and poaching the land as they starved, could now be housed and fed adequately on turnips, straw and hay, and their dung spread on the land as fertiliser in spring. This simple cycle was a revolutionary concept. So little was the value of dung as manure understood in Orkney earlier in the century, that Pringle had been scandalised to see it thrown out of byres into the sea![18] The "high farming" practised by Traill and some of his contemporaries aimed at high output by feeding purchased oil-cake to produce more meat and more dung to spread on the fields to promote high yields of grain and fodder.

½ ton of oil cake £6 7s 6d
2 qrs feeding lintseed £0 8s0

is a typical accounts entry in 1871. Artificial fertilisers also became widely used in this period, and there is not an issue of *The Orcadian* or *The Orkney Herald* of the 1860s and 1870s that does not advertise Manures ("of great benefit to turnips"), Dissolved Bones ("always in great demand") or Best Quality Peruvian Guano.

In 1868 Traill paid £51 18s 10d for manures (a sum equivalent to the annual wages of four farm servants) and in 1870 £45 for manures and another £8 12s 6d for a ton of dissolved bones. The huge sums involved indicate the scale of an "improving laird's" investment in agriculture.[19] There are also frequent references to cargoes of "Scotch Lime" or "English Lime" which he imported to the island in his own schooners, the *Margaret Traill* and *Mary Traill* to improve his land. In 1866, for example, £11 1s 0d was paid for 102 bolls of Scotch Lime.

From 1866 onward statistics of crops and livestock are available as a result of the annual agricultural census organised by the Board of Agriculture. The Agricultural Returns for Westray and Papay show that the acreages of the traditional crops, bere and oats, were increasing at this time and that Traill even attempted to grow wheat on Westray; 46 acres were sown in 1866 but this was evidently not a success as it was never tried again.[20] The new crop husbandry made a complete break with old-style farming. Instead of bere and oats being grown incessantly on the same land as in the past, allowing no opportunity to clean the ground of weeds or for the exhausted soil to recoup fertility, cereals were now grown in rotation with artificial grasses and turnips. The combination of rotation, liming, improved drainage and cultivation techniques, the use of dung and artificial manures, produced far heavier yields than in the past, and the five year rotation of oats, turnips, oats, grass, grass remained, with modifications, the basic pattern of husbandry on most Orkney farms for over 100 years.

Turnips (the acreage of which increased until about 1890) provided the all-important winter fodder for cattle, allowing more beasts to be kept and fattened to far heavier weights. With introduced grasses and clovers, and artificial fertilisers, the quality of the grassland could also be much improved and there was a considerable annual outlay on seed for the new crops; (in 1869 Traill bought 60 lb of turnip and swede seed and paid his merchant £31 8s 6d for clover and rye seed). The tenant farmers were also encouraged to follow the laird's example. From 1867 onwards new items in George Miller's account show that the modern husbandry was being practised at Cuppin:

4 Bush. Rye @ 3s, 10 lb Rib Grass @ 4d	
4lb Red Clover @ 8d	**18s 0d**
4lb Green Top Yellow Turnips @ 8d	
1lb Swedes @ 9d	**3s 5d**

Better feeding, as well as the introduction of improved strains of livestock from Scotland, meant that cattle, sheep and horses improved in size and quality. "The cattle are chiefly shorthorn crosses, and come out heavy in the hands of Mr Traill and others. The sheep are crosses of the Leicester ram with the Cheviot ewe".[21] The small native sheep which used to roam everywhere were banished to the Holms, but even these Traill improved with imported Shetland stock. At the time of the displenish sale in 1889 Holland was running 43 half-bred ewes, and using both shorthorn and black polled bulls on its 28 "milch cows". These were not dairy-type cows but were milked and a considerable amount of butter was made on the farm. That this was a far superior item to the "grease butter" in which tenants formerly paid their rents is shown by the large quantities which Traill shipped down to Leith in his schooner. In December 1863 he exported 13 jars containing 505 pounds of butter, 377 pounds going to private customers in Edinburgh.[22]

The agricultural revolution benefited from the rapid advances in technology in the 19th century. The development of better iron and steel meant that farm implements could be made which were stronger, lighter and more durable, and the ground could be cultivated more efficiently. New designs for mechanising threshing, reaping, hoeing and all the other laborious manual tasks were being invented and improved upon rapidly, and the latest designs in iron ploughs, horse hoes, turnip drills and reapers were quickly installed at Holland. Horse-drawn reapers were available in Orkney in the 1860s (the Holland accounts for 1871 include "reaping machine . . . £26 19s 6d"), but the binder did not reach the islands until the 1890s. From the 1850s onward a full-time blacksmith was employed at Holland, and it is unlikely that farming has changed so greatly that he was not extremely busy repairing machinery all through the urgent seasons of hay and harvest.

WOOD'S NEW IMPROVED ONE AND TWO HORSE
REAPING MACHINES,
WITH SKELETON DROP PLATFORM.

Price, ONE-HORSE (including extras) £15 0 0

Price, TWO-HORSE (including extras) £16 10 0

Extra Knife (sent with each Machine) £1 0 0

These Machines are now so well known in the North that it seems superfluous to publish testimonials in their favour. The SUBSCRIBER, however, has permission to refer to the following, among other Gentlemen, who have for some time had them in use, and who express themselves as perfectly satisfied with the manner in which they perform their work, viz.:—

Archer Fortescue, Esq. of Swanbister.
James Cromarty, Esq. of Bankburn.
Messrs Flett of Redland.
Spence of Hall of Rendall.
W. Cromarty, Widewall.
W. Banks, Melsetter.
D. Munro, Saverock.
James Heddle, Greenwall.
John Paul, Sanday.
James Watson, Orphir.
W. Scott, Tukquoy, Westray.
W. Stevenson, Holland, Stronsay.
W. Learmonth, Elsness, Sanday.
Thomas Drever, Tressness, do.
John Mackay, Warsetter, do.
Andrew Thomson, Gerbo, do.
James Swanson, Hammerbreck, do.
John Irvine, Stove, do.
James Clark, Barns, St Ola.
William Tait, Campston.
Samuel Haddon, Birstane, St Ola.
J. & R Gibson, Langskail, Rousay.
Andrew Muir, Seater, Sanday.
William Stocking, Clifton, Westray.
Benjamin Clouston, Keigar, Deerness.

CHARLES DAVIDSON, KIRKWALL,
AGENT for ORKNEY and SHETLAND.

Kirkwall, May 1871.

The great interest - and investment - in farming in the 1860s and 1870s is evident in the number of front-page advertisements for agricultural implements, seeds and manures in the local papers. *(Courtesy of The Orkney Herald)*

As soon as he had got improvements underway on the home farms, Thomas turned his attention to creating new farms out of the hill and heathland. Tenants were encouraged by low initial rents to break in new farms from the common and to replace their turf-roofed cottages with the larger, stone-slated dwellings and byres that still stand today. Jeremiah Seatter started to create Hundland in 1847, gradually reclaiming 25 acres of arable land from the North Hill and building a house and steading. In Westray a large farm was created at Gallowhill, where a fine steading was built and 700 acres of land reclaimed from former commonty, which "gives good crops, under Mr Traill's high farming".[23] In 1848 he had already bought 1,200 acres of commonty land in Holm on Mainland Orkney and in the next 10 years, by draining, liming and enclosing, had reclaimed 450 acres of New Holland.[24]

The enclosing and reclaiming of common land was, of course, a contentious issue. If a few tenants benefited by the opportunity to make, by their own back-breaking toil, a piece of land they could farm, other tenants resented the loss of their higgledy-piggledy acres when these were "tidied" into Holland's new square fields, or the loss of their Hill grazing when part of the Hill was reclaimed for new farms. (This issue would later feature frequently in complaints to the Crofters Commission. Thomas

Harcus of Midhouse, for example, claimed that 100 acres of the North Hill had been withdrawn from the common grazing).[25] On the whole, however, the tenants benefited from the encouragement they received to improve their own homes and farms, the increased opportunities for casual employment, and the high prices they received for their own stock during the "boom years".

They must also have benefited from the enormous changes made in Papay (and elsewhere in Orkney) to the traditional system of paying rent. George Traill regularised the onca ("on call") services to a specific number of days work which were calculated as part of the rent and, by the time that Thomas inherited, his rents from his 32 tenanted farms on Papay were assessed partly in money, (£2 - £8 a year each, depending on their acreage), but also in poultry (worth 6d each), six days work (worth 1s a day) and sometimes meal or butter. In practice the cash value of the rent, and other goods which were obtained from the laird, was invariably paid in kind (usually in kelp or butter) or in labour.

In 1844 Robert Irvine's rent for his 13 acre farm Hinsobrae was money rent of £4 14s, plus seven bolls bere, three poultry and six days work. He paid in:

6 caisies corn @ 11s	£3	6s	0d
75 lb butter @ 6d	£1	17s	6d
26 weighs 12 st ware kelp	£3	8s	9d
(roughly 2½ tons)			
17 weighs 6 st tang kelp	£1	14s	9d
(roughly 1½ tons)			
3 poultry @ 6d		1s	6d
6 days work @ 1s		6s	0d
	£10	**14s**	**6d**

One of the larger farms, Quoys (21 acres), was rented at seven guineas, plus five poultry and six days work. The tenant, David Groat, paid the poultry and labour and made up the balance in corn, butter and kelp. These were typical rent accounts, but a few of the tenants could offer other labour skills instead of working at the unpleasant task of gathering and burning kelp. In the same year Benjamin Burgar was charged £2 money rent for Daybreak, plus one lispund and four marks butter (roughly 31 pounds), and he paid in butter, in 38 days farm labour and by weaving 42 ells of cloth (worth 10s 6d). In 1850 David Miller of Midhouse was credited £1 1s 11d for making and mending sails for a skiff.[26]

The fact that, besides his full-time farm servants at Holland, Thomas Traill could command a plentiful supply of cheap casual labour from amongst his tenants was an important factor in his improvements. The island was densely populated at this time (the population of Papay reached its maximum level of 392 in 1861), and as the farms were far too small to provide subsistence for a family and the rent, almost every able-bodied man and woman on the island was at some time of the year working for the laird to gain a livelihood. Their meagre wages are meticulously recorded in the Holland rent books and the change in the rental is noticeable as Papay's agricultural revolution gets underway. Although kelp remains an important item, butter disappears and an increasing proportion is paid in livestock and in construction work. Rents had been paid since medieval times in "grease butter" and its disappearance from the Holland rents in 1850 marks a radical departure from the past. From the 1850s onwards there is a gradual change from a kelp-based to a livestock-based economy, with most of the tenants paying part of their rent in cows, oxen, sheep and pigs, and making up the rest in labour. In 1863, for example, Robert Irvine pays his debts with "1 quey . . . £4 4s 0d". By the 1870s and 1880s another innovation has entered the rent books: part of the payment is made in money.

The remarkable transformation which "improving lairds" such as Thomas Traill wrought in their estates in a mere quarter century was summarised in a report which one Westray proprietor gave to Farrall, a contributor to the 1874 issue of *Transactions of the Highland and Agricultural Society of Scotland.* "Twenty-five years ago there was very little sown grass; no rotation . . . very few turnips grown; and no extra manures used . . . No scythes or reaping-machines to cut corn - nearly all done by the serrated sickle. Farm-servants received £5 to £8 per year; women, £3 . . . No iron ploughs, and very imperfect wooden ones. Sheep small, weighing 20 to 30 lbs, and ran at large upon the hills. Two-year-old cattle sold at £2 10s to £3; now they sell at £10 to £15 . . . This year I got 30s each for my Leicester Cheviot lambs, £15 for my two-year-old cattle, and £26 for a young mare . . . There were no good roads in the country; now we have good hard roads through every parish and island . . . we have also a steam-boat twice a week through the North Islands, which has raised the price of all farm produce down to eggs. They are now 9d per dozen, and I well remember the time when selling them at six for a penny."[27]

Thomas Traill's dykes and gate pillars are a feature of Holland *(Inga Hourston)*

The "New Hooses" c. 1900. The last family moved from here in 1955 and the houses fell into dereliction until their renovation by the Papay Community Co-operative as a guest-house and shop, opened in 1980.

V

Worthy of his Hire

'Seventy years I've had of this', said Ward.
'Going in winter dark
To feed the horse, a lantern in my fist,
Snow in my beard,
Then thresh in the long barn
Bread and ale out of the skinflint corn,
And such-like work!'
George Mackay Brown, "Farm Labourer"

In the last half century agricultural progress has been almost synonymous with the replacement of humans by machinery, but the revolution which Thomas Traill and his contemporaries brought about was only possible because labour was so plentiful at that time. The modernisation of the farm required a huge amount of manpower to perform the manual tasks of quarrying stone, dykeing, road-making, drain-cutting and building, and even when these were completed a large permanent work force was needed to cultivate the increased acreages of arable land and harvest the increased yields of crops. 19th-century mechanisation transformed some of the most laborious tasks of the past (the horse-powered threshing machine replaced the threshers with their flails, the horse-drawn reaper the shearers with their sickles), but the new system of husbandry was still extremely labour-intensive. Large farms like Holland employed 10 or a dozen regular servants, and many more on a casual basis, and it would not be until the mid 20th century that agricultural mechanisation, and a new type of farming, would seriously displace people from the land.

With his full-time servants living on the farm, the Holland which Thomas inherited was home to an astonishing number of people. At the time of the 1841 census, Holland House itself was a crowded and lively establishment which the young laird shared with his mother, six brothers and sisters and their maternal grandfather, a visiting preacher and three house servants and five female farm servants. Crowded around the steading were another 11 houses. The miller and his family lived in the cottage beside the barn; in the bothy six lads of 14 or 15 years old slept two or three to a box-bed. Mary Miller "washer and dresser", her children and John Scott, a joiner, lived in Holland No.6 and two fishermen and their dependants in Holland No.7. Six other houses were inhabited by farm servants and their families. In all there were 72 people living at Holland! [1]

In the next census "the gentry" were still resident amidst a great number of servants and labourers. In 1851 Thomas Traill, then aged 29, proudly gave his occupation as "Landed Proprietor Farming 837 acres employing 35 Agricultural Labourers". He and his wife Margaret and two small children were living in Holland with six female servants and there were still 10 other houses occupied on the farm, one by a joiner and his young apprentice, one by Mary Miller, Cook, and the others by farm servants and their families - a total of 56 people. The grieve's house was now occupied by John Mackay and this was a significant appointment. This was to be the last census in which the Traill family were found living at Holland, and it seems that after this Thomas was increasingly leaving the management of the farm in the hands of managers and grieves.

Only the mansion and grieve's house are still inhabited of the 10 or 11 houses that were at Holland in the mid 19th century, though many survive as farm buildings. An old lady was remembered who was "born in the midden of Holland" but the houses which appear on the 1879 ordnance survey map in this unsavoury location were long ago demolished. The upgrading of Holland into a model farm of the 1850s obviously involved a great deal of reorganisation of both buildings and people, and something of the massive changes that took place here mid-century is evident in the next census.

The picture of Holland in 1861 is entirely different. The big house stands empty, save for a single housemaid, and John Mackay's grandchildren are the only children living on the farm. Five unmarried men live in the bothy and Mary Miller and her son and a single under-dairymaid live in the two remaining cottages. All the rest of the farm servants have been relocated to a neat terrace of six two-room cottages at a genteel distance from the house, each with its own kail-yard in front. Two more cottages house the blacksmith and the miller. An entry in the Cash Book confirms that these were already under construction in 1850 when John Drever of Bilboa was credited

> "By his supposed share of building houses for servants,
> 4 of them say £1 15s 0d . . . . .£7 0s 0d"

The "New Houses" were probably an enormous improvement in living standards from the insanitary hovels clustered around the Holland midden, but the silence of the big house is an ominous indication that Traill is starting to abandon his role of "improving laird" for other, more expensive interests. It is six years after this census that we first find him taking out a large mortgage on the estate.

Like many other landed proprietors, Traill imported managers and skilled labourers from other parts of Scotland, where farming was more advanced. Top of the list was James Walker, whose social standing can be deduced from the fact that he earned £100 a year for managing the Brough and Gallowhill estates. Well below him in financial status was John Mackay, who came from Caithness to be grieve at Holland for 35 years. Alexander Cleugh and Donald Henderson were also brought from Caithness for their skills in shepherding flocks of Cheviot sheep.[2]

Holland farm in Thomas Traill's time was more than twice its present size and occupied about one-quarter of the island. Beyond its boundaries, still defined by Traill's stone dykes and gate pillars, was the land of his tenants - his casual labour force. At the time of his sequestration there were 42 small farms, mostly 10 to 20 acres in extent, on Papay and another 32 on his Westray estates. With the croft tenancy went access to the common grazing, which at this time included the South Hill and East Hill as well as the North Hill, and with this privilege most families were able to keep one or two cows and a few sheep as well as cultivating two or three acres of arable ground.

The old bothy, now a museum.

The laird had total control of the economy of the island and it is noticeable in the rent books how much more complicated this economy became in the second half of the 19th century. In the book covering the years 1844 - 1851 the tenants are debtors only for their rent, and with the kelp and butter they produce the accounts are neatly balanced at the end of the year. In the 1850s and the 1860s they are increasingly indebted for commodities which Traill imported in his own schooner and in return for which he took their stock at his own valuation. Some of these are the agricultural supplies necessitated by modern farming methods, such as lime and manures, turnip and clover seeds. Then there are the barrels of coals imported from Newcastle and the foodstuffs - beef and mutton and oatmeal - which perhaps imply a slightly better standard of living than in the past. There are also all the debts to Holland farm: the blacksmith's account, or for extra grazing in the corner of a field, or the service fee for a mare at horse (a hefty 10s). In the 1870s it is evident that the tenants are failing to pay their accounts, and the sum of their arrears is growing year by year.

When farm produce was selling at peak prices the standard of living of tenants as well as proprietors improved with a small cash income in most households, but as the prices of livestock fell in the late 1870s, they found themselves trying to pay ever-rising rents out of a declining income. Their holdings were so small that the most they could produce to sell was one or two calves a year, and perhaps a couple of lambs, and even growing crops for subsistence was difficult when their few acres could not support the horse or oxen needed to draw a plough. Their problems were compounded by their vulnerability. Although there was no programme of eviction on Papay, no discontented tenant had the secure possession of his home, or the option of anywhere else to go. The insecurity ceased with the passing of the Crofters Act in 1886, but land-hunger

JAS. R. GARRIOCH, Stromness.

EMIGRATION TO

OTAGO, NEW ZEALAND.

ASSISTED PASSAGES GRANTED TO AGRICULTURAL LABOURERS, SHEPHERDS AND THEIR FAMILIES, AND FEMALE DOMESTIC SERVANTS.

SHIP "AGNES MUIR," FIXED FOR 13TH APRIL.

As the demand for Labour continues to be great, and the Rate of Wages for AGRICULTURAL LABOURERS, SHEPHERDS, and FEMALE DOMESTIC SERVANTS exceptionally high in this Province, the Provincial Government have instructed their Home Agent to continue to grant ASSISTED PASSAGES to those classes, which he is prepared to do on most favourable terms.

Messrs P. Henderson & Co's. beautiful Clyde built Clipper Ship, "AGNES MUIR," A 1 at Lloyds, 20 years A 1 in Liverpool Book, 850 tons register, will Sail from GLASGOW for OTAGO direct on 13TH APRIL.

This splendid Passenger Ship has superior Poop Accommodation for Cabin, and lofty and well ventilated 'Tween Decks for Steerage Passengers, with all the modern improvements.

A duly qualified Surgeon will accompany the Ship.

Parties eligible to receive assistance, and others intending to pay their own Passage Money, will receive full information on applying to

GEORGE ANDREW, Secretary.

OTAGO OFFICE, 60 PRINCES STREET,
EDINBURGH.

Advertisements such as this one from *The Orkney Herald*, 1869, lured many young people from their over-crowded small farms to the promise of greater opportunities in the colonies.
(*Courtesy of The Orkney Herald*)

remained a problem on the island until well into the 20th century, when it was gradually "solved" by depopulation rather than by government intervention.

Many lairds like Traill, who had invested heavily in their estates at a time when profits seemed set to rise for ever, foundered with the agricultural recession. The routine farm work of course continued normally but there were no longer the major building projects which had allowed many of the tenants to earn a cash income to pay the rent. Increasingly they left their cramped farms to seek a living elsewhere and the population of the island fell steadily. Emigration overseas was encouraged by the weekly advertisements in *The Orcadian* and *The Orkney Herald* of assisted passages for skilled labourers or domestic servants emigrating to Australia, New Zealand and Canada. Some were bitterly disillusioned by what they found, and their disappointment is made more poignant by the fact that they had literally bought a one-way ticket. John Baikie wrote to his relatives in Daybreak, Papay from Vancouver Island in 1852 of the false promises held out to emigrants, ("I never thought much of this Place since first I came here"), wishing he could come home but unable to as he had loaned out money which was not repaid.[3] Others, like Robert Seatter of Hundland, had happier experiences. Robert, a carpenter, paid £13 for an assisted passage to Dunedin in 1874 and established himself successfully in New Zealand with his Papay-born wife. Stories of a world where land and opportunity was plentiful filtered back to relations and friends at home and encouraged them to follow.

The Holland tenants continued to press demands for more land until the time that the estate was broken up in 1922 and they were able to buy their own farms, but the census shows that by then the pattern of continued emigration and smaller families had considerably reduced the pressure on the land. In 1921 the population was down to 247, and its decline was never arrested.

While Thomas Traill was enjoying the soaring profits from his farms, the wages of his labourers rose at a much more moderate rate. When he took over the estate in 1844, male labourers were paid one shilling a day. In the 1850s and 60s men could earn one shillling to two shillings a day for quarrying stones, carting and breaking stones for roads, building dykes, digging drains, unloading the schooner, thinning turnips, working at the mill, as well as the usual seasonal tasks of sheep-dipping, hay-making and harvest. Boys earned sixpence a day for gathering stones or weeds off the fields, or cutting thistles. By 1880 there was far less construction work happening, but for general agricultural work men earned two and sixpence or three shillings a day. Women received eight pence to one shilling in 1844, for hay and harvest work, lifting potatoes, thinning turnips, working kelp and spinning wool. Forty years later, women were still hiring for one shilling a day! [4]

In 1871, when Traill sold stots for over £23 a head, and bought a bull for £32 10s 4d, his foremen at Brough and Gallowhill earned £12 a year. Mackay, drawing a grieve's salary of £16 in 1859, was still earning the same amount in 1875! As a comparison, while in 1880 the price of a single beast would pay a skilled Orkney labourer's wages for a year, 100 years later it required the price of 15 to 20 beasts to pay a farm worker. While farm wages remained low, food prices were not proportionally cheap. Most families

Farm-servants at Holland in the 1880s. 13 men and three women appear in this rare formal group of farm staff. The man seated centre may be John Learmonth, the manager, originally from East Lothian.

supplemented the diet of oatmeal porridge, beremeal bannocks and potatoes by fishing. Any foodstuffs that they purchased (beef at 4d a lb, cheese at 3d a lb, mutton at 8d a lb, butter at 1s 3d a lb in the 1880s) must have been luxuries on 15s to 18s a week.

The full-time servants at Holland were paid an annual wage with an allowance of meal and sometimes coal or potatoes. In 1860 a female servant earned £4 a year plus two bolls of oatmeal, two bolls of beremeal and three barrels of potatoes. A man earned on average £10 a year, with three bolls each of oats and beremeal and five barrels of potatoes. Craftsmen were rather better paid: David Miller the blacksmith earned £15 in 1860 with meal and coal; Alexander Cleugh the shepherd had a rent-free house, keep for a cow and two tons of coals beside his cash wage of £12, the usual allowances of meal and potatoes, and extra oatmeal for his dog. At the same time his employer was running up debts to the tune of more than 1,000 times Cleugh's annual income.

***

VI

End of an Era

The farmer ploughed and reaped,
Led five lean harvests in,
The young men long away:
There was a great war then.
Edwin Muir, "The Breaking"

By 1886 Thomas Traill's creditors had had enough. With his debts running at over £32,000, he was declared bankrupt and his property was sequestrated. (The scale of Traill's debt was enormous; at that time £32,000 was the value of 2,000 prime beasts, and would have paid the £35 a year salary of his farm manager Learmonth - himself earning two to three times as much as an ordinary farm servant - 914 times over. The annual rent of all his tenant properties in Papay, £479 4s 6d, would only have amounted to such a sum after 67 years!) Holland then entered a very different era. For the next 36 years the estate was in the hands of trustees for his principal creditor, William Baird of Elie, and Holland was leased to tenant farmers.

It seems to have been a rather bleak time for the farm and for the island as a whole. As the Trustees did not have outright ownership of the estate but held it as security for Traill's debts, they resisted any attempts for development or change. (By refusing to allow the Papa Westray Parish Council a plot of land on which they could build a house for a doctor, for example, they made it virtually impossible for them to attract or keep a resident doctor on the island for 30 years).[1] There was constant and bitter land agitation, and a running battle between the Crofters Commission, supporting the tenants' demand for enlargement of their holdings, and the Trustees, stubbornly refusing to part with any of Holland's land. There was no further investment in the farm and there was criticism of its mismanagement. The Great War took its toll of casualties from the island.

In June 1889 the Trustees advertised the Traill farms for lease. *The Orkney Herald* carried the advertisement:

1.The HOME FARM OF HOLLAND, Papa Westray, extending to 418 acres or thereby, mostly arable, along therewith the two MEAL MILLS of PAPA, and the HOLM of PAPA, extending to 47 acres or thereby, all pasture, suitable for sheep.

2. The MANSION HOUSE of HOLLAND, Papa Westray, partially furnished, GARDENS, LAWN and OFFICES, with the SHOOTINGS on the island and on the HOLM of PAPA, and the Estates of BROUGH and RAPNESS, in Westray. Excellent fishing. Rent Moderate. Entry immediately, and to be let for the season or longer. [2]

The advertisement clearly hopes to tempt a sporting laird. The Trustees had visions of filling the empty rooms of the mansion house with smart shooting-parties, but this was an almost pathetic attempt to recall a bygone age. Many proprietors had been hard-hit if not bankrupted by the recession, affluent sporting gentry were hard to find

WALL, WEDNESDAY, OCTOBER 9, 1

HOLLAND, PAPA WESTRAY.

EXTENSIVE AND IMPORTANT DISPLENISH SALE.

The Subscriber begs to intimate that he has been favoured with instructions from the Trustee to Sell, by Public Roup, at HOLLAND, PAPA WESTRAY, on TUESDAY, October 22nd (with continuation of days if necessary), the whole large and valuable FARMING STOCK and IMPLEMENTS thereon, belonging to the Sequestrated Estate of Mr TRAILL of Holland, comprising :—

HORSES.—3 Superior Work Horses, 6 Work Mares, from five to eleven years old ; 1 aged Mare, 1 Three-Year-Old Filly, 1 Two-Year-Old Colt, 1 One-Year-Old Filly, 1 Mare Pony (aged) ; 1 Horse Pony (two years old).

CATTLE.—1 Superior Black Polled Bull, three years old ; 1 Shorthorn Bull (red), two years old ; 1 Shorthorn Bull (roan), two years old ; 1 Cross Polled Bull Calf (red), 7 months old ; 4 Milch Cows (farrow) ; 24 Milch Cows in Calf ; 4 Two-Year-Old Heifers in Calf ; 30 One-Year-Old Cattle ; 28 Calves.

SHEEP.—43 Half-Bred Ewes (all young) ; 2 Cross Tups, 1 Blackface Tup.

PIGS.—1 Sow, 6 Young Pigs.

POULTRY.—12 Geese, and a large number of Ducks and Hens.

Also, the whole of the very large assortment of FARMING IMPLEMENTS, HARNESS, &c., &c.

The s.s. "ORCADIA" will leave Kirkwall on the morning of the day of Sale at 7 A.M., calling at Stronsay, Sanday, and Eday (Calfsound). Sale to commence immediately after arrival at Papa Westray. The steamer will return same evening, and will call again at Papa Westray on Thursday morning (24th).

Four Months' Credit on approved Bills for sums of £10 and upwards.

T. SMITH PEACE, Auctioneer.

IMPORTANT SALE OF FURNITURE.

There will be Sold, by Public Roup, within the TEMPERANCE HALL, KIRKWALL, on MONDAY, Oct.

An advertisement of Holland's Displenish Sale in *The Orkney Herald*, October 9, 1889.

and unprofitable agricultural estates were no longer attractive. All over Orkney farms were being broken up, and the notice of Holland's displenish sale appears in *The Orkney Herald* four months later amongst columns of similar farm sales.[3] Holland farm and the house were let to Thomas Cumming of Cleat in Westray for £202 10s 0d per annum rent; Brough and Rapness were let separately to farming tenants.

Ten years later the Trustees attempted to recoup the entire debt by auctioning the Traill properties in Glasgow for the upset price of £33,000.[4] The sale was advertised in August 1899 but apparently the estate attracted no offers and in 1900 it was put on the market again, this time for £30,000, with Papay advertised as a most desirable investment. "There is an excellent Home Farm with commodious Mansion House, Gardens & lawns attached, all presently let on lease. Rental £623 16s 6d exclusive of income from kelp. The property forms a fertile, compact and picturesque residential estate with ample facilities for sport."[5] Despite all the estate agents' blandishments, the excellence of the shooting, the potential income from kelp and fishing, the efficiency of communications with the recent extension of the telegraph service to Westray and the thrice-weekly steamboat service, there was still no purchaser. It could hardly have been a worse time to sell an agricultural estate. Farming no longer seemed a sure investment, and the Crofters Act of 1886 had fettered the landlord's power over his own estates in a way which undoubtedly made landholding much less attractive, as well as less profitable. The Crofters Commission had halved the rental from Traill's Papay and Westray farms, and the subsequent slump in land values held them almost static for the next half-century.

So Holland remained in the hands of the Trustees, with Cumming living in the mansion house and running the farm. He does not appear to have been a particularly efficient farmer and his poor management fuelled the resentment of the land-hungry tenants of the small farms. As they were applying to the Crofters Commission for enlargements of their holdings at the expense of Holland, they obviously had an axe to grind, and perhaps they exaggerated the decline of Holland in Cumming's hands when they described it as overstocked with cattle and understaffed with men and horses. In 1904 Cumming had a serious gig accident which left him permanently disabled. A sad picture of the man is conveyed in his increasingly shaky signature to the minutes of the Parish Council meetings, which he chaired until 1909 when another hand tersely records his death.[6]

Cumming's widow Margaret "carried on with her grieve" (in one of the memorable phrases in which local history is transmitted), Robert Bain, and continued the lease. She soon re-married, to John Petrie of Westray. As residents in the mansion house and tenants of the largest farm, the Petries seem to have been anxious to fill the vacant role of laird, and from this time onward island memories flesh the bare bones of historical records. J D Mackay (great-grandson of the grieve John Mackay) remembers Petrie visiting the school during the war to deliver lectures on Patriotism. "After his talk, the pupils were marched round the playground four or five times while they sang 'Rule, Britannia'. Mr Petrie was not a very good singer and he often went out of tune".[7]

Mrs Petrie dined in state at the east end of the house while all the farm workers ate in the kitchen at the west end. A suspicious soul, she ordered all the supplies of beremeal

Hay-making at Holland in 1913. Robert Bain, the grieve, is second from the right.

and oatmeal to be carried out of the meal-loft and up to the attic bedrooms to prevent the servants stealing them. One of her maids, Maggie Stout, treasured the memory of how she and another servant lass had taken revenge on Mrs Petrie for her meanness. Tired of being allowed only the worst of the butter, they had taken the butter jar destined for sale in Westray, removed a large helping for themselves and replaced it with their rancid butter. The jar, with its innocent top layer of good butter was despatched and, Maggie gleefully recounted some 60 years later, Mrs Petrie could never understand why the order for butter from Holland was suddenly cancelled!

In 1922 a Decree of Foreclosure deemed Thomas Traill's heir to have forfeited the right to redeem the sequestrated estate.[8] His creditors were now sole proprietors, and Baird's Trustees immediately set about disencumbering themselves of the property. The estates of Papa Westray and Brough in Westray were immediately put on the market in one lot for an upset price of £14,000 - the Papay estate including "the Home Farm of Holland, one of the best in the County . . . and 55 other possessions of £96 rent and under." [9] The sale marked the end of an era for Holland and for Papay as a whole - no one was interested in buying the island as a private estate and it was the last attempt to keep it as one. The farm and house of Holland were bought by William Frederick Brown of Breckowall in Westray, but he did not wish (or could not afford) to become laird to the "55 other possessions". The Trustees subsequently sold Brough separately, and the small farms to their tenants.

Between 1924 and 1927 all the Papay crofters purchased their farms and became owner-occupiers - a transition that was happening all over the county. In the post-war depression agricultural estates throughout Britain slumped in value and, unable to meet the burdens of death-duties and increases in rates and income tax, many disintegrated. The unsuccessful attempts to sell the Holland estates between 1889 and 1922 were echoed all over Orkney, with estates intermittently on the market and finding no buyers. Eventually most of these, like the very large Sanday and Stronsay estate of the bankrupt James Traill of Hobbister, were disposed of in the 1920s by breaking them into small parcels and selling them to their sitting tenants, and even in this form they sold slowly. Although the tenants were able to purchase their farms for an almost nominal price, farm incomes had fallen so low that they often struggled to raise even this.[10]

Nonetheless, there was a very significant change in the pattern of landownership. Thomson observed that "the break up of big estates and the conversion of tenants to owner-occupiers overturned the very structure and basis of Victorian Orkney. It brought about more fundamental changes in land tenure than had ever resulted from the feudalising of incoming Scots and their attacks on the odal system."[11] While in 1920 more than 90 per cent of the farm land in Orkney was rented, by 1930 this had dropped to 33 per cent. By an irony of history, the land was again in the hands of small owner-occupiers, as it had been before powerful families like the Traills succeeded in amalgamating freehold properties into large estates in the 17th century.

The Smithy and Workshop *(Inga Hourston)*

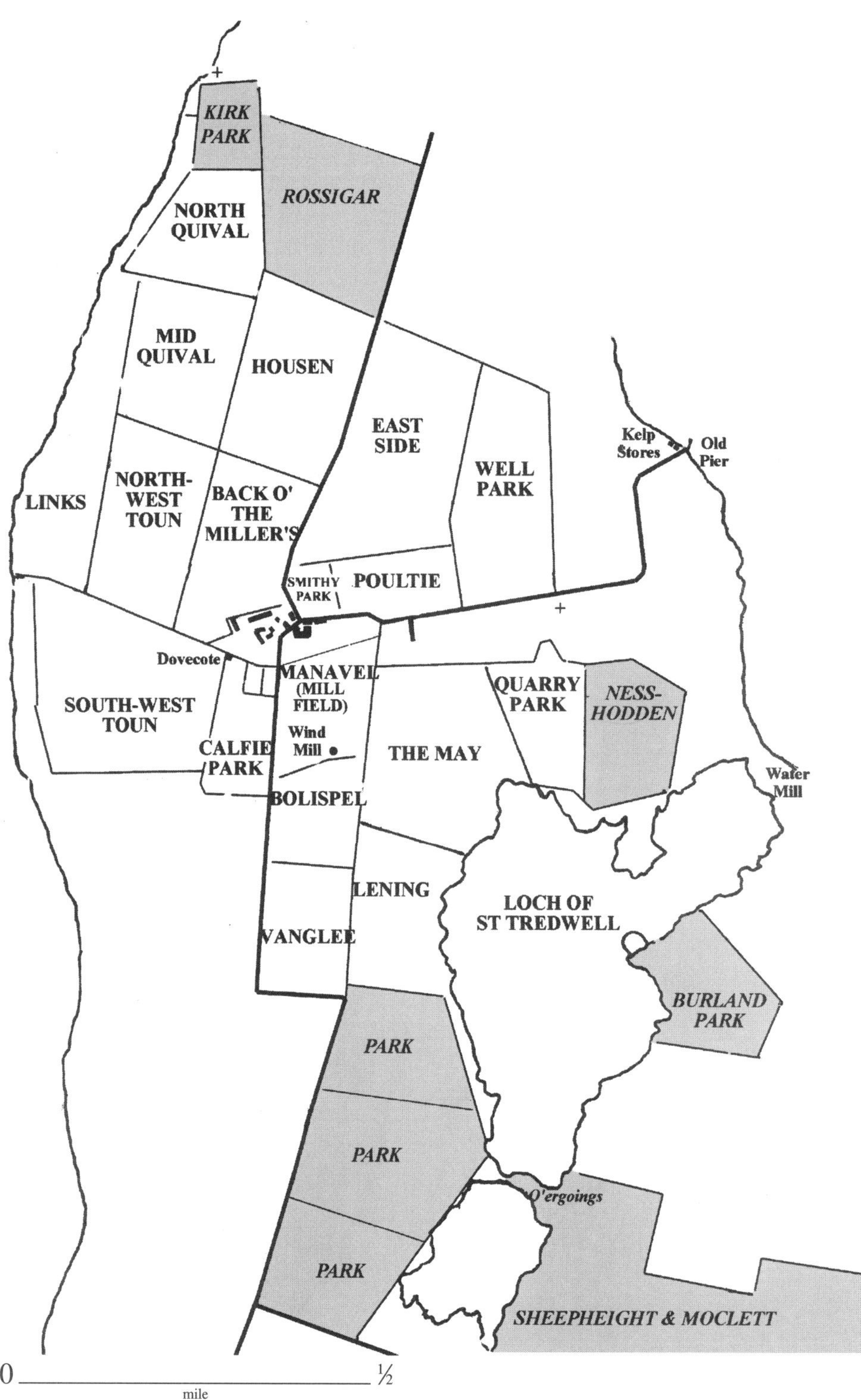

Holland Farm in 1886.

Fields taken by the Crofters Commission for croft enlargements 1889-1908

Aerial view of Holland Farm from the south, September.

Holland House from the walled garden created by George Traill c.1830, June.

Neil Rendall taking Shetland rams to the Holm in the dinghy, November.

Holmie Day, July.

Lifting tatties in the May beside St Tredwell's Loch, September.

View across Eastside, August.

Aerial view of the Knap of Howar, September.

VII

Crofters

(Parliament) robs me of about 3,000 acres of my land, which has been taken from me without compensation and has been handed over in perpetuity to a class of persons called Crofters . . .
General FW Burroughs

Thomas Traill's bankruptcy fell in a momentous year for landlords and their tenants: 1886 saw the passing of the Crofters Act, an event which was to have an enormous impact on estates in the Highlands and Islands. The years between the sequestration and the break-up of the Holland estate were characterised, above all, by what Thomas might have called the "Crofter Problem".

The late 1870s and early 1880s were lean years all over rural Britain due to the agricultural recession. In Ireland the poor seasons and falling prices of 1879/80 led to rent strikes and outbreaks of violent agitation, with tenants maiming landlords' livestock and smashing machinery. A frightened Parliament passed the Irish Land Act of 1881 which provided for security of tenure and judicially determined rents. In the Highlands bad harvests in 1881/82, the drop in wool and cattle prices and the failure of the East Coast herring fishery combined to create a feeling of desperation among tenantry too often thirled to meet ever-rising rents with decreasing means. At the same time the success of the Irish Land League in bringing about land reform inspired hope that change could be forced in Scotland. Riots broke out in Skye and Gladstone's government panicked at the prospect of a repeat of the Irish situation. In 1883 a Royal Commission was appointed to investigate causes of grievance and distress amongst the crofting population.

While the Napier Commission took evidence around the Highlands and Islands the crofters awaited its conclusions with little hope of redress and the lairds with little anxiety. The Commission was drawn solidly from the landed classes; Lord Napier, former governor of Madras, was a Borders landowner; Donald Cameron of Lochiel, Tory MP, owned 110,000 acres in Inverness-shire and Sir Kenneth MacKenzie of Gairloch 164,000 acres in Ross-shire; Sheriff Alexander Nicolson and Charles Fraser Mackintosh came from landed families. Most of the gentry assumed that the Commission would "vindicate many sorely maligned proprietors and factors from the charges made against them by untruthful outside agitators."

In fact, the findings of the Napier Commission led to the passing of an extraordinary Act of Parliament which sanctioned an unprecedented government interference in the relationship between landlord and tenant. The Crofters Holdings (Scotland) Act of 1886 allowed crofters security of tenure on their holdings and the right to assign it to a near relative on their death or retirement, the right to a fair rent which would be fixed by a Crofters Commission, and the right to receive compensation for any improvements they made to their holding if they left it. More than a century later, these provisions seem so commonplace that it is easily forgotten just what a radical piece of legislation this was.

Even to the more liberal-minded of the landed classes in the 19th century, property rights were absolute and almost sacrosanct, and for the government to interfere and dictate the manner in which a landlord ran his own property was both politically revolutionary and morally outrageous. The diminutive figure of General Burroughs of Rousay, effervescing with fury at the Napier Commission hearing, is legendary in Orkney history but there is little doubt that his outrage expressed the feelings of most of his fellow lairds. Burroughs felt betrayed both by his tenants, who had dared to criticise him in public, and by the government who had actually supported their sedition. In his view the crofters' desire for security was a gross infringement of property rights. "What can they have unless they wish to rob us of our land?"[1] Given the resistance to the Bill from the landed interest who were so heavily represented in Parliament, it is amazing that the Crofters Act made it to the statute book.

The Orkney proprietors panicked and summoned an emergency meeting in the Kirkwall Town Hall on August 10, 1886. Bristling with righteous indignation, they drew up a document to demonstrate that no part of Orkney could be construed as a crofting parish, and therefore the Act did not apply to them. *The Orcadian* published the document, and the opposition "at once took steps . . . to prove that the various parishes in the county were crofting parishes within the meaning of the Act". The Commission found for the crofters, and all over Orkney they started to file their applications for fair rents.[2]

The responsibility for administering the Act across the widely scattered communities of the Highlands and Islands fell on just three men, David Brand the Sheriff of Ayrshire, Mr Hossack of Oban and Mr McIntyre of Ross-shire. The speed and diligence with which they worked can be judged by the fact that in August 1888 they reached Orkney and within six or seven weeks disposed of 443 applications for fair rent and several applications for extension of holdings, inspecting 6,124 acres of arable and 3,176 acres of outrun in the process. By September 10 they were interviewing the Westray and Papay tenants in the United Presbyterian Kirk in Westray.

The statements given by the 40 Papay crofters are terse, but shed a fascinating light on the changes they had witnessed in their lifetimes: in nearly every case they or their fathers had built their houses and steadings and reclaimed some (or even all) of their land. Their complaint was invariably that their rents had been raised although they had lost land and common pasture as the result of the reorganisation of the estate and their holdings were too small to be viable. Most of the Papay crofts were less than 20 acres in extent and often supported two or three households - a feat only possible, as the crofters' lawyer Andrew Thomson pointed out, because of "industry at the fishing". The knife-edge economy of the small farms, with their one or two cows, and two sheep, and - the lucky ones - a horse, can be glimpsed in a sample of the statements.[3]

The chief grievance of the crofters was not so much the rents as that their crofts were too small to provide a living for a family. In many cases the few acres would not support a plough-team of two horses or even a horse and an ox, and there was barely enough land for subsistence, let alone to rear animals to sell. On an average-sized croft John Davidson of Southhouse kept one cow, one quey, one native sheep, one mare and a foal. At Gowrie Andrew Harcus could keep two horses and two cows but very few farms had more than this. Most of the crofters were compelled to make kelp in order to pay the rents.

The statements made by the Papay crofters to the Crofters Commission were published in Kirkwall the following year by W R Mackintosh. "Jeremiah Seatter, Hundland, had 25 acres arable, and 15 of outrun... He had been 39 years in the place, and had reclaimed all the land and built all the houses . . . Andrew Harcus, Gowrie. . . had 2 cows, 1 one-year-old, 2 calves, 2 horses and 2 lambs . . . He had broken in 9 acres, and built byre, stable and out-house, and enlarged the dwelling-house . . . In 1868 ½acre of his best land was taken away, and in 1879 the rent was raised . . . A part of the North Hill was also taken away . . . Nicol Robertson, North Rendall, was an old man who remembered when the South Hill was common to the whole island. It was then taken away . . . John Drever, Cott, had 16 acres of arable, and 3 of outrun. He paid £20 of rent in money, 3 days work, and poultry valued at 5s . . . His rent had been raised from £14 since 1868 to the present rent of £20 for the same land, with the exception of ½ acre he had lost. George Miller, Cupping, had 20 acres arable and 4 of outrun. He paid £12 of rent and was £30 in arrears. He had occupied the place for 27 years, and built a dwelling-house and steading, at a cost of £80. In 1880 the rent was raised from £9 10s to £12, and 2 acres of land taken off. Sheriff Brand: I never saw an estate where the allegation was made so frequently that the rent had been raised and the land taken away."

Some of the entries mention a peculiar circumstance of this estate, that a number of the tenants were owed money by the bankrupt Traill, for livestock or labour for which they had never been paid. "Andrew Drever, Daybrake, said he had 6 acres arable, and 1 acre outrun. He had 2 cows and 1 sheep, but had to buy feeding for one of the cows. . . He was a creditor on Mr Traill's estate to the extent of over £247. . ." Together the crofters on Papay alone were creditors to the tune of £400. One man was actually a registered pauper on parish relief while being owed £56 by Traill!

On every Orkney estate the Commission had found the rents unreasonably high, but on the Holland estates they found that the rents had also risen faster than anywhere else in the county. When Fair Rents were fixed, on average the rent of Orkney estates was decreased by 30 per cent and 44 per cent of arrears cancelled, but the Holland rents were decreased by 46.5 per cent and 79 per cent of arrears cancelled. It must have been a great day of rejoicing on the island.

Although the Crofters Act was of enormous significance, it did not really please anyone. Its provisions outraged landlords, but did not go nearly far enough to solve the crofters' demands for land. It had the powers to fix fair rents, but its powers of making more crofting land available by forcing the division of large farms were very limited. It could not assign land for croft enlargements from farms that were already let on lease, or from farms with a letting value of under £100. The proportion of a large farm that could be assigned was limited to from one-third to two-thirds, depending on its total rent. The Commissioners had to be satisfied that the land the crofters applied

Jeremiah Seatter and his wife, Isabella, created the new farm of Hundland from the North Hill. In his evidence to the Crofters Commission in 1888, he "had been 39 years in the place, and had reclaimed all the land and built all the houses."

for could be assigned "without material damage to the letting value of the remainder" of the farm, and "without substantially impairing the amenity" of the farm residence or steading. There was therefore plenty of scope for landlords' objections and interminable haggling.[4]

The Papay crofters were, therefore, extremely fortunate in the timing of the Commission. In 1888 the estate was in the hands of Trustees for the creditors and had not yet been leased to a tenant, and so the Commission had the power to insist on enlargements. Despite the resistance of Mr Gibson, the Trustee, and Mr Drever, the estate's agent, they ordered that three of Holland's parks south-west of the loch, approximately 20 acres each in size, should be subdivided to provide enlargements for 13 crofters. The fortunate ones were those whose land lay south of Holland and near to the new fields. The application of six other crofters for land north of Holland was refused on the grounds it would "materially damage the letting value" of the farm.[5]

It must have been reconsidered, however, for in 1892 four of these applicants (the crofts of Roadside, Clestrain, Hinsobrae and Mayback) were granted the 24 acre park of Rossigar. News of their victory must have reached the crofters before Cumming heard that he was to lose one of his best parks, for there is a cherished story of Tammo o' Clestrain seeing the Holland farm servants working in Rossigar and saying "I think you should go hame to pleugh your ain land". Evidently the Trustees had bowed to pressure from the Crofters' Commission to create more holdings and resigned themselves to also losing the rest of Holland's ground south of the loch. As well as giving 18 acres to the croft of Blossom and six to Vestness, they made an entirely new farm. When the estate was advertised for lease in 1889, Sheepheight with the Links of Moclett was offered as a separate property of 84 acres.

The bankrupt Thomas Traill must have followed the events taking place on his sequestrated estate with aggrieved interest. As he had ruined himself before the arrival of the Crofters Commission, he could hardly blame the government for doing so, as General Burroughs did, but he could not have viewed the compulsory re-allocation of his land among his tenants with equanimity. In a letter to Charles Traill of Ulva in New Zealand (formerly his neighbour at Westness), Burroughs wrote that he and his uncle had laid out £40,000 in improvements on the Rousay estate. "I laid all this money out in the expectation of getting a fair return for it and thus laying by a provision for my old age. As old age is creeping on parliament steps in and robs me of the expected return for my outlay. . . You will understand now why I am anxious to sell my Estate while I have any portion of it I can call my own and before I am robbed of it all!"[6] Burrough's plaintive lament conveniently ignored the plight of his evicted crofters in *their* old age, but undoubtedly fellow lairds like Traill felt similarly outraged.

Inevitably, the enlargements of a few crofts only fuelled the determination of the remaining tenants, and for the next 30 years there was a constant rumble of demand that Holland should be divided. In the absence of a laird, there was no traditional respect for "the gentry" to hold frustration in check and with only a tenant occupying Holland, it was inevitable that land-hungry men on their pinched crofts should look enviously at the great acreage concentrated in the hands of one man. In 1908 a further attempt was made to gain enlargements, the crofters backing their claim by pointing to Cumming's mismanagement of the farm.

> "At the beginning of winter it is common for some of the animals at Holland farm to be left out in most unsuitable weather because there are no houses for them. A reduction of land would remedy this. . . The farm at present is and has been all through the present tenancy, beyond the strength of men and horses kept to cultivate it. To overtake the work men and horses have to work exceptionally hard in all sorts of weather to their injury, and to the injury of the soil,. . . which was avoided by former grieves on the farm. . .(The farm) is not yielding anything like what it used to do when farmed by the late proprietor under his skilful manager. . .the farmer of Holland cannot get his work done without assistance from the crofters every year - in laying down and singling turnips - reaping and leading the crop. . ." [7]

A map drawn up by the Crofters Commission in 1908 shows that during the previous 20 years Holland had lost 237 of its 621 acres. Besides the 82 acres of enlargements to existing crofts made by order of the Commission in 1889 and 1892, 155 acres had been given by the estate "voluntarily" for the creation of new farms and enlargements. In 1908 the crofters applied for a further 88 acres of Holland's ground for enlargements, and were granted by the Commission the fields furthest from the steading (Nesshodden, Kirk Park, Burland Park and an 18 acre park south-east of the loch), about 42 acres in all. The application for North Quival, Vanglee and Lening was rejected and Holland was left in possession of 342 acres.[8]

In 1906 a new Liberal government had come to power which was dedicated to the principles of land reform and in the following years the landed interest was desperately trying to defend its position against legislation aiming to reduce the chronic land-shortage by settling smallholders on the large estates. In 1911 the Small Landholders (Scotland) Act gave the Board of Agriculture powers to carry out schemes for creating holdings on privately owned land. When landowners refused to co-operate, the Board could apply to the new Scottish Land Court for an order authorising the constitution of new holdings. The Court also determined compensation due to the landowners for devaluation of their land (a card which the landowners played hard), and took over from the Crofters Commission the authority to fix fair rents. In practice the Board was hampered by loopholes in the legislation which allowed landowners to drag out expensive arbitration over compensation claims, by a restriction on touching farms over 150 acres, home farms and farms under lease at Whitsunday 1906, and by a chronic shortage of staff.[9]

By the end of the First World War the government was embarrassed by its own propaganda promise that servicemen who had enlisted voluntarily would be given grants of land on their return. Throughout the Highlands and Islands demand for land was clamorous but there was an almost total lack of effective machinery to acquire or provide it. Although the 1919 Land Settlement (Scotland) Act gave the Board of Agriculture new powers to purchase lands by agreement or compulsorily, its workings were so cumbersome and could be so easily thwarted by uncooperative landowners that there were endless delays in purchasing farms and very little settlement.

Until the moment the estate was sold, the crofters, William Baird and the Board of Agriculture wrangled inconclusively over Holland. In 1913 the Commissioner for Small Holdings reported to the Board that he was satisfied "that there is a demand for Small Holdings in the Parish of Papa Westray and that the farm of Holland is available to meet the demand and is suitable for the purpose." He had endeavoured to negotiate with the landlord, William Baird, but as Baird refused to allow any new holdings, the Board of Agriculture laid their scheme before the Scottish Land Court.[10]

The Board's scheme demanded a drastic carve-up of Holland's remaining land. One hundred and two acres were to be divided amongst 15 existing crofters and two new holdings were to be made from a further 11 acres. Holland would lose all the fields not immediately adjacent to the steading. As usually happened in these cases, the resistance of the landlord protracted the negotiations and it was not until January 1920 that the Land Court formally dismissed the application.[11]

Evidently by this time the Board had changed tactics and decided to attempt to purchase the whole farm. Mrs Petrie's lease was coming to an end in 1922 so as that time drew near Holland must have seemed very suitable for acquisition. In 1919 the Board drew up plans for dividing Holland's steading and 160 acres of its land among three farms (sharing the Holm as common pasture), and utilising the rest of the land to enlarge 19 holdings. This was superseded by another plan in 1922 for dividing the farm into four larger units and 17 enlargements. Worthy as the idea was to provide several working units, the plan of the divided steading is a futuristic nightmare, showing the kiln barn, mill tramp and all the more historic buildings demolished and the remainder a blue-print for neighbourly dissension.[12] The Board did purchase and sub-divide in this way the farm of Stove on Sanday, and the close-packing of three independent farms and families within a single steading was apparently not a recipe for harmonious living!

One of the returning servicemen who qualified for a settlement grant was George Rendall, who was demobbed from the navy in 1919 and came home to marry Isabella Miller of Cuppin. He was promised the New Houses as a farm and meticulous plans were drawn up for dividing the six cottages into an admirable self-contained house and steading. He must have been bitterly disappointed when the plan was withdrawn and the whole farm put on the market in June 1922. By a nice irony of fate that George would have thought inconceivable, he was to live to see his son John and grandson Neil become the owners of the whole of Holland.

***

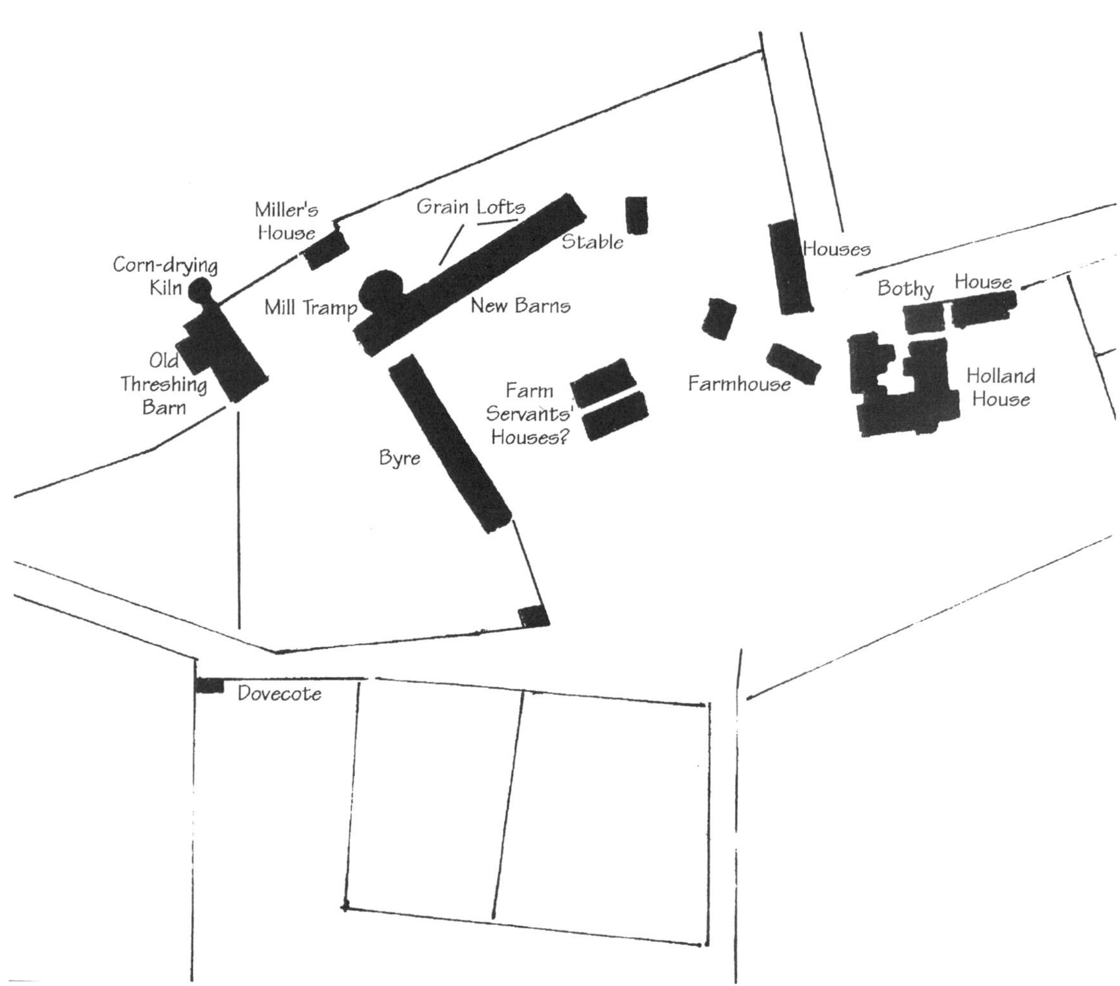

An 1844 plan of Holland, based on the estate map made for Thomas Traill.

VIII

A Story in Stone

Nothing contributes more to the content and conveniency of a farmer, than good and well disposed buildings
Dr James Anderson

The intransigence of William Baird saved Holland from the dismemberment planned by the Board of Agriculture. In 1922 the farm was sold to William Frederick Brown of Breckowall in Westray, trimmed to less than half its original acreage and no longer the hub of a substantial estate, but with its houses and extensive steading still intact.

The demands of modern agriculture have not been kind to farm buildings and relatively little has survived of the splendid "model steadings" of the mid 19th century. In the second half of the 20th century tractors and implements outgrew even the largest barns; byres designed for manual feeding and cleaning were found hopelessly unsuited to modern, less labour-intensive, systems; and threshing barns, kilns and grain lofts gradually became obsolete as grass almost entirely replaced the traditional grain crops. Many 19th-century steadings survived intact for 100 years or more simply because there was no surplus money to invest in replacement, but disappeared as better farm profits and government grants made it possible to build new agricultural buildings. Another factor was the number of people who left farming after the Second World War, which led to many farms being amalgamated and surplus steadings, such as the lovely farm that Thomas Traill built at Gallowhill, abandoned to dereliction.

Through various accidents of history Holland has been more fortunate in its survival rate than most Orkney farms. It never had a planned farm courtyard such as Traill built on new sites at Brough and Gallowhill in the 1860s because it already had substantial 17th- and 18th-century buildings which were incorporated into Traill's new steading. In fact Holland's owners have added to it piecemeal in times of expansion and prosperity over almost four centuries. Like many other farms, it remained unchanged during the inter-war depression years, the old buildings being adapted to new functions rather than replaced, and only in the late 20th century was significantly modernised and enlarged with new byres, silos and implement sheds. The sheer scale of these has of course altered the appearance of the farm but, by enabling it to survive economically, they also made possible the preservation of a rich architectural legacy in agricultural buildings.

No map of Holland survives from earlier than 1844 so reconstructing the farm that the first lairds knew is partly guesswork. It seems likely that the attractive cluster of tall grey buildings at its centre, with their stone slate roofs and corbie-stepped gables, belonged to the 17th-century property that the Traills purchased from Thomas Scollay. Behind the old farmhouse stand two other dwellings, which perhaps once accommodated animals on the ground floor and servants in the upper rooms but for long have been used as stores - a process of declining down the social scale which is a characteristic fate of rural buildings. Older still is the small "staigy house", once a stable and now a store but the fireplace and windows suggest domestic use and tradition remembers it as the kitchen of the long-vanished farm Manavel. (The size of the door leaves one in no doubt that the staigs, or stallions, in question were in residence before any horse larger than a thin pony was kept at Holland!) The flagstones with their beautifully tapered overseamers, which probably replaced an earlier thatched roof, are very characteristic of Papay and Westray building tradition.

The "lectern-style" dovecote is 17th-century in style and so probably one of the early additions that the Traills made to their property. Pigeons were valued as a source of fresh meat, a welcome change from the interminable winter diet of salted meat, and for their dung for enriching the soil. A dovecote was also something of a status symbol as an Act of the Scots Parliament of 1617 limited their building to landowners with land of an annual value of 10 chalders (around 10 tons) of grain lying within two miles of the cote,[1] (to prevent the predations of domestic pigeons on other people's grain). The stone slates from the dovecote were removed in 1928 to repair another roof, but many of the nesting boxes remain.

Farm buildings are far less prone to changes in architectural fashion than domestic ones and so notoriously hard to date on appearance alone, but the west barn seems to be another survival from the first generations of the Traill lairds. Once the largest and most important building on the farm, the crops of oats and bere were threshed here by flail and winnowed, the opposing doors in the middle of the building creating a through-draught to carry away the chaff. As needed in the winter, a stack of corn from the nearby stackyard would be dismantled and loaded on to a cart, the sheaves pitchforked through the upper door in the gable end to a half-loft at the south end of the barn and thrown down from there to the central threshing-floor.

At its north end the barn terminates in the characteristic bottle-shaped corn-drying kiln where the grain was dried by the heat of a slow fire drawn through a flue from the barn. The grain was laid on a bed of straw resting on kiln-sticks which in turn rested on the ledge which runs round the interior of the kiln. Access to the grain is by a flight of stone steps from the barn, the narrow passage roofed with stone lintels reminiscent of the architecture of the brochs and a striking reminder of the continuity of stone building traditions in Orkney. The steps on the outside of the kiln allowed access to the loose flagstones covering the vent, which could be moved to adjust the draught. Kilns were vital in Orkney, as the wet climate made it impossible in most years to produce grain dry enough for milling without recourse to artificial drying, and this is one of the largest farm kilns in the county. Possibly the unusually long passage was a safety measure, distancing the grain in the kiln from the fire in the barn, for kiln fires were always a hazard. The North Isles Presbytery Records relate that in 1718 the people of Papay begged the minister to hold a weekday fast to pray for the end of a calamitous outbreak of cattle disease. Thomas Traill (the third laird) refused to allow his servants to attend the Kirk, "but in the just judgement of God, when the Minister came by the said Holland's house going to the church, his kiln went on fire." Thomas was so alarmed by the swift retribution of the Almighty that he despatched his servants to the Kirk with all speed![2]

The corn drying kiln.

The fortunes made from kelp by lairds like George Traill (the sixth laird) financed a building boom in Orkney. George spent some of his kelp profits on a more fashionable new house at his ancestral seat, and built an attractive two and a half storey, L-shaped mansion, linked by a single-storey service wing to the old farmhouse which George utilised as servants' quarters. This became a kitchen with a laundry above, (the huge box mangle, in which the maids laboriously pressed the gentry's linen, is still there). The main rooms on the ground floor were the drawing room and a long library occupying most of the east wing. Children (George had eight), and maids were accommodated in the attic and there were also box-beds for female farm servants in the small loft above the service wing. The new house was made more impressive with a formal approach: a gravel drive swept from the entrance, the "gentry slap", past the walled garden which George created, to the front door, flanked by neatly laid out lawns and orchards.

George started the work of enclosing fields at Holland, but his most significant innovation on the farm was the horse-powered threshing engine. It was recorded by a contemporary, Walter Traill, in 1823 and so one of the earliest in Orkney and its arrival at Holland must have caused huge excitement. Horse-engines were normally driven by either two or four horses harnessed to a central wheel, connected by a system of cog-wheels to either an overhead or an underground shaft which turned the drive-belt of the threshing mill in the adjacent barn. In later engines the mechanism was entirely made of iron and the drive-shaft was usually sunk in a channel below the open-air paved area "tramped" by the horses. The cog-wheels on earlier engines were made of wood and the circular "mill tramp" buildings were designed to protect the machinery

The conical roofs of mill-tramps posed interesting problems for the carpenter.

from the weather. (The timberwork of their attractive conical roofs posed interesting problems for the carpenter, every roof has a different structural solution!) They had the disadvantage that the horses - probably four for large engines as at Holland, harnessed in two pairs - became over-heated with the exertion of working the mill, and the six openings in the building maximised the ventilation in an attempt to overcome this problem.

Open-air tramps or horse-courses continued to power threshing mills on the smaller farms in Orkney well into the 20th century, but at Holland the horses were replaced by a petrol/paraffin engine in the 1890s. The mill tramp found successive uses, at various times housing cattle, pigs, implements and hay, and the mill itself continued in use, tractor-powered, until 1992. I like to think that Robert Rendall's poem *The Horse-Mill* may have been inspired by the mill tramp at Holland.[3] The poet was a friend of William Traill and visited him in Papay several times.

Beside the heavenly meadows daisied with stars,
The planets yoked in team - Uranus, Mars,
Jove, Neptune, Venus, Mercury, Saturn, Earth -
Not saddled now to run with tightened girth,
But to the mill's unwieldy lever bound,
Wheel their enormous burden round and round.
Linked to the trees, harnessed with hame and trace,
They stumble round the tracks of cosmic space,
With slow hard step, necks bent, and flanks a-sweat
Turning yon beam, the sun for axle set.
To grind what corn in what celestial mill
Move these great Titans, shouldering onward still?[2]

Next to the mill tramp stands the miller's house (in later times a "byre for sick cattle" and then a piggery), and the field behind it is still known by the long-winded name of Back o' th' Millers.

The huge two-storey barn which Thomas Traill built replaced the west barn and dominated the 19th-century steading. The threshing mill rises through both floors at the west end and straw and hay were stored in the middle, where there was a hoist for lifting sacks of grain up to the grain loft which ran above the stable at the east end. At a later date the centre bay was also floored to increase the storage area for grain. In the summer the grain lofts were empty, and the 100 foot-long loft space provided - and still provides - a dance floor for island weddings and celebrations. It also has a surprisingly good acoustic for concerts (when a summer storm is not rattling the roof slates), and it may have been the first time for several centuries that a song written by "Germany Thomas", *O My Love's in Germany,* was heard at Holland when it was sung here by Emma Kirkby in 1990.

Most of the oat crop was used for cattle feed during the winter, but the oats and bere for human consumption still had to be ground into meal. There was a watermill on the island from at least the 17th century, when Thomas Traill bought "the milns of papa with. . . the haill astricted multures of the haill island"[4], (in other words, his tenants were compelled to have their corn ground at his mill, and had to pay him a portion of their meal for the service). As there are no other water-courses on the island the mill has probably always stood on its present site at the outflow of St Tredwell's Loch. The flow of water led from the loch could be dammed by a sluice-gate, creating a build-up of water and so greater pressure to turn the undershot wheel when it was released, but probably there was rarely sufficient water to work the mill efficiently. With the great increase in grain production in the mid 19th century there was need to improve the farm's milling power. Thomas Traill (7th laird) rebuilt or enlarged the watermill for grinding oats and also built a windmill for grinding corn (bere). This was a post-mill, of which only the stone base survives. In order to turn the sails into the wind the whole timber superstructure was revolved on this base, by means of a long tail-beam which was wheeled around the mill. The wages for work on the mills appear in the Holland accounts:

1864 John Reid, Whitehow
18 days work at mills @ 2s   £ 1   16s   0d
making sails for mill 90 yds @ 2d   15s   0d
1865 David Groat, Dyke
building 42 fathoms of dyke at windmill @ 7d   £1   4s   6
George Robertson, Edgeriggs
12 days building pillar of windmill and work at watermill
8 days 2½ hours work at Do. @ 1s 9d   £1   15s   5d
1866 16 days building at Cornhouse @ 2s   £1   12s   0d
1867 Thomas Drever, Ness
9 days building at Cornhouse @ 2s   18s   0d

The north range of the steading built by Thomas Traill, with grain lofts above the threshing barn, hay barn and stables.

Despite the hefty expenditure of £8 the windmill did not have a long life. By the early 20th century both mills seem to have fallen out of use and Holland was taking its grain to commercial mills on other islands to be ground.

The alterations to the steading made between the 1844 estate plan and the first ordnance survey map of 1879 are not visually very significant but they do mark changes in agricultural practice during the period of "Improvements". A turnip shed added to the west byre reflects the shift to growing root crops for cattle feed. New byres suggests increased numbers of stock, and now enclose that hallmark of agricultural improvement, a midden. Another addition is the "sheepie houses", indicating concern that the new, larger breed of sheep imported from the Scottish mainland would not cope with the Orkney climate without cosseting! Pringle wrote in 1874 that in Orkney "great pains are bestowed both upon the (Leicester-Cheviot) ewe and her progeny in the breeding season. Indeed, many farmers place the sheep under cover every night in winter, giving them a plentiful supply of straw; and in the daytime, turnips are thrown to them upon the pastures"[5] (In time it was discovered that Cheviot ewes survive even the Orkney winter outside, and the "sheepie houses" fell into ruin). The great increase in the use of machinery and in building activity necessitated the employment of a smith and a joiner among the full-time staff, and by 1879 two cottages have been converted into a smithy and a joiner's workshop.

The conversion of the old houses into workshops and stores was made possible by the relocation of the married farm servants to the "New Hooses" in the 1850s. The farm was no longer a busy dwelling area (as it clearly was in the 1841 census) and the only employees living on it were the manager or grieve, who had his own house, and the young unmarried men and boys in the bothy. Simply furnished with two box-beds and remembered as damp and smoky, the old bothy next to the "oxy byre" could never have been anything but cold, dark and smelly and, when extra men from Westray were staying for hay-making or the hairst, distinctly crowded. The bothy-men did not cook for themselves, as was usual on large farms in north-east Scotland, but ate in the servants' kitchen of Holland or the grieve's house. In 1928 William Traill renovated the hayloft above the "young horse stable" as a rather more salubrious bothy with wood-lined walls and an iron stove. Farm buildings are endlessly recyled: the last occupant of the new bothy, John Rendall, has restored the old one as a museum.

Surprisingly, the next major addition to the steading was built after the bankruptcy of the Traills' and during the tenancy of Thomas Cumming, when the Trustees and the Crofters Commission were wrangling endlessly over the division of Holland. In 1899 the construction began of the long "kye's byre" and "calfie byre", the only building roofed with imported Welsh slate rather than stone slate, which tidied the spraggling steading into a square and greatly increased the cattle accommodation. Ahead lay long decades of agricultural depression and it was over 70 years before there were any further changes to Holland.

Diagram of a mill tramp in action

(Courtesy of The Royal Commission on the Ancient and Historical Monuments of Scotland)

Only the stone stump survives of the windmill built in 1864/65 for grinding corn.

An impression of the windmill when it was in use. The whole superstructure could be revolved with the aid of the wheeled tail-beam. *(Inga Hourston)*

IX

Hard Times and Iron Horses

Wooden harvesters do not sing harvest songs; iron mowers do not drink from cold springs . . . the poets and the prophets are a brotherhood, but the poets and the profits are strangers, for ever.
19th century American

In 1922 the Petries retired to Fribo in Westray and their foreman Robert Bain retired also, to spend the rest of his days, it was said, gazing across to Papay from Westray and pining for Holland. The farm was in the hands of its new owner William Brown and heading for the economic depression of the years between the wars.

The First World War had totally dislocated life in rural Britain. Socially and economically its effects were traumatic and irreversible but temporarily, agricultural areas like Orkney had benefited from the high prices for farm produce. The policy of depending on imported food, the main cause of the agricultural recession of the 1870s, had made Britain very vulnerable in time of war. Food shortages resulted from the naval blockades and by 1916 retail prices had risen to 60 per cent above their pre-war level.[1] The government shared the prevailing optimism that the crisis would soon be over and was slow to take effective measures to increase home production. However, in 1917 incentive schemes were introduced to bring more ground into tillage and farmers were obliged to follow cropping directions issued by the Department of Agriculture. The Corn Production Act guaranteed minimum prices for wheat and oats and fixed minimum wage rates for agricultural workers. In fact, the food shortages forced prices and wages far above these levels, but a significant precedent had been established with the government's intervention. R Perren summarised the situation in *Agriculture in Depression 1870-1940:* "From 1917 onwards agriculture became a controlled industry, with government direction of production, while at the same time the marketing of farm products became essentially a government monopoly, and the consumer was protected by price and other forms of control." [2]

For three years after the First World War farmers continued to enjoy their high profits. As a result of the economic chaos in post-war Europe, full employment at home and poor harvests in 1919-20, agricultural prices rose as much as 26 per cent between 1918 and 1921.[3] In that year food imports resumed on a massive scale and grain prices crashed to half their previous level. The government decided it could not afford to pay the guaranteed prices and repealed the Corn Production Act. British agriculture sank into a prolonged depression far more serious than that of the late 19th century and which hardly improved until the Second World War.

In peacetime British markets, unprotected by tariffs, could not compete with the expanding economies of America and Asia. There were world surpluses of all internationally traded agricultural products and, as European countries increased

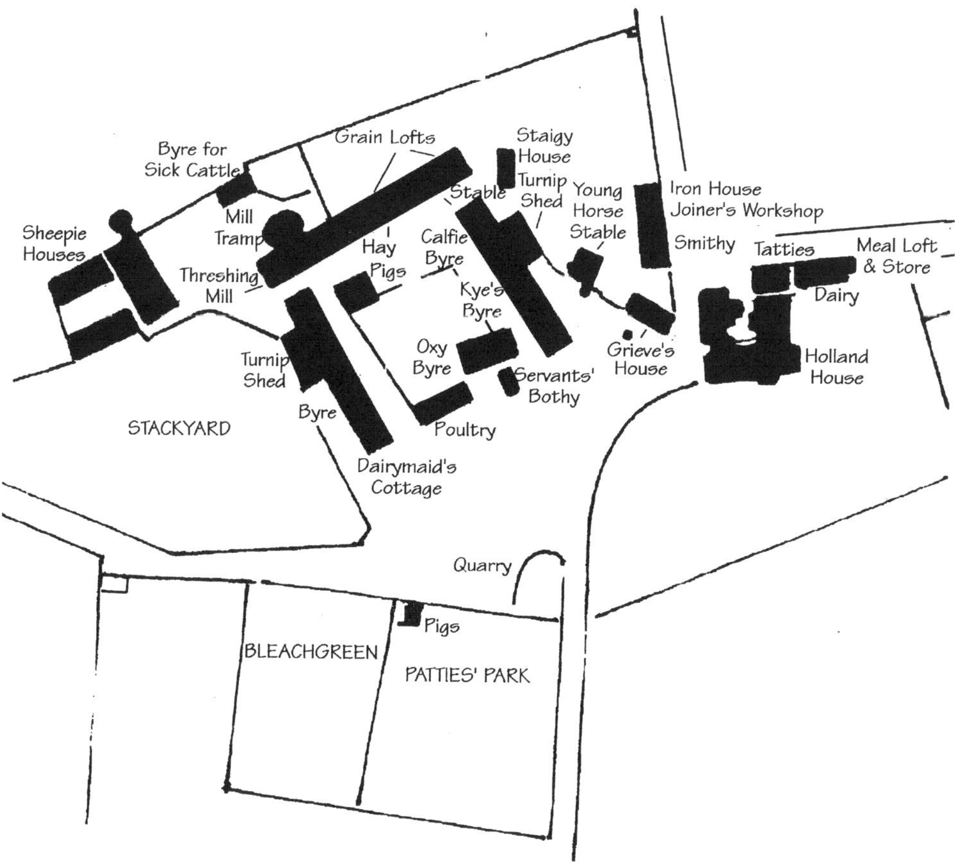

Plan of Holland in 1920.

protection for their own agriculture, more and more food over-supplied the markets of the remaining free-trade countries. Britain became a dumping ground for foreign produce at a time when high industrial unemployment and economic hardship kept consumer demand low. The 1920s saw meat imports rise by 44 per cent and livestock prices fell so severely that farmers were unable to sell fat cattle or sheep except at a loss. By 1929 they were competing against over £103 million of grain, meat, fruit and dairy produce imported from the rest of the Empire. [4]

The 1931 and 1933 Agriculture Marketing Acts introduced some support to British farming in the form of subsidies and these and the gradual spread of mechanisation increased farm output in the 1930s, but prices remained low. There was a steady drift of farm workers from the land, encouraged by the higher wages and shorter hours offered elsewhere, and a steady exodus of landowners, the rural employers and investors, as their inheritance became increasingly burdensome and unprofitable. Orkney suffered less than some parts of the country from the real hardship that accompanied the Great Depression. Most people were at least able to fish for or grow some of their food and virtually every farm had a share in Orkney's phenomenally successful egg industry which cushioned the impact of falling incomes from livestock. A few of the larger

William Frederick Brown of Breckowall, Westray, sowing neeps. Brown was owner of Holland (1922-28), and then tenant (-1941). *(Orkney Library Photographic Archive)*

Mainland farms were able to start introducing more up-to-date methods and machinery, but for most it was a time of difficulty with little financial incentive for innovation.

Brown was unfortunate in buying Holland at the time when high prices were still prevailing in the immediate post-war years, and rather rashly paid £4,250 for the farm. A disastrous first harvest immediately landed him in financial difficulties, and after that farm prices sank. (Oats which had sold for £14 a ton during the war fell to £4, for example, beef fell to £2 a cwt, about one-sixth of its wartime value).[5] In 1923 we find him giving a bond for £3,000 to the Union Bank of Scotland on the security of the farm,[6] and soon after he is selling off small houses and fields in separate parcels. A way out of his difficulties appeared in the form of William Traill, who in 1928 bought Holland but left Brown as tenant of the farm.

William Traill was the fourth son of the bankrupt Thomas. His three older brothers had already died unmarried before they could fulfil their dream of repurchasing the family home, but one of them, dying in Africa, left him money on condition he bought back Holland for the Traills. J D Mackay has left an amusing pen portrait of Willie Traill. "His features were heavy and when he scowled his somewhat ferocious expression would strike terror into the hearts of small boys. When irritated . . . from his mouth there would issue a volley of oaths designed specifically to shock Kirk elders and other godly persons".[7] Mackay remembers him as a brilliant raconteur, mingling tales of Victorian Orkney with jungle tales from Burma where he had spent much of his life as

Abby Brown and his Clydesdale stallion, *Noltland Castle.*

(Orkney Library Photographic Archive)

The Holland farm servants in 1924. Back row: George Rendall (Big Geordie), James Rendall, John Hourston, James Bremner (the manager). Middle row: George Rendall, not known (the blacksmith), Johnnie Harcus. Front row: Abby Brown, George Rendall (Old Geordie), and John Robertson, who died the following year from tuberculosis.

a civil engineer. He was also a keen naturalist and antiquarian and amassed one of the best private libraries in Orkney at Holland. As a young man he had excavated St Tredwell's Chapel and the Iron Age site beneath it and in 1930 he and his friend William Kirkness (an art teacher at Stromness Academy and, like Traill, a Fellow of the Society of Antiquaries of Scotland), conducted the first excavation of the Knap of Howar.

William Traill lived at Holland House until his death in 1944, and was succeeded briefly by his only married brother, John, and then his nephew Thomas. Tom Traill and his family had little interest in living in Papay and the property had become a financial burden. When the hurricane-force gales of January 1952 and 1953 ravaged the buildings, he was glad to sell the farm for whatever he could get for it.

This was the final exit of the Traills from Holland. A curious situation then arose with regard to the ownership. Throughout William Traill's time, the farm had been let to tenants who farmed through a succession of managers. While William Brown tenanted Holland he lived in Westray but his son-in-law James Bremner and then his son Abby managed the farm. When Brown died in 1941 the tenancy was taken over by John Scott, but in 1945 he moved to his Mainland farm and managed Holland through his foreman, John Hourston. He was a Papay man who had worked all his life on the farm. His wife Maggie Stout had come from Westray to be servant to the Petries and eventually became housekeeper to William Traill. The farm market was depressed

Farm servants cleaning the quarry, 1926. ***Left to right:*** **James Bremner, Geordie Rendall, Willie Gray, John Hourston.**

and there were no offers for the farm when it was put on the open market, so in 1954 the Hourstons and their son-in-law John Rendall from Cuppin, a farm servant at Holland, bought the house and land. Lacking the money to buy the stock and machinery as well, they continued working as servants to John Scott, their tenant! When Scott gave up the tenancy in 1967 the Rendall family took over the stock at valuation and from then on owned the farm outright. The farm is still in the hands of John, his wife Annie Jean and their son Neil - from 1980 onwards, the partnership of Rendall and Son.

Throughout the tenancies of William Brown and John Scott Holland's evolution followed a pattern typical of livestock-with-arable farms all over Orkney. The word "followed" is deliberately chosen and marks a significant change of tempo. Although Holland was still much the largest farm on the island and an important employer, it was no longer playing a leading role. While owned by a wealthy laird enjoying the profits of an agricultural boom, it had been one of the most modern of Orkney farms, but the situation in the 20th century was very different. For nearly 80 years after Traill's sequestration Holland was in the hands of tenants, who were often financially overstretched by owning other farms and hampered by the agricultural depression. (A stark glimpse of farming financial returns in the first half of the century is evident in the rents: in 1941 Scott was paying the same rent for Holland as Cumming had paid 50 years earlier, £200, or £80 less than Holland had been valued at in 1881!)[8] The result was a lack of investment in the farm; there was not one new building put up between 1900 and 1974 and Holland was slow to catch up with the mechanisation that occurred on most of the larger Orkney farms after the First World War. It was a long period of conservatism, in contrast to the innovations of the previous century.

Hay-making, 1926.

This large group of 1926 hay-makers includes a number of men from Westray, as well as every available man and boy from Papay.

Although mechanisation was speeding up agricultural tasks between the wars, the traditional system of husbandry remained the same. Since the mid 19th century Orkney farming had been geared primarily to the production of beef cattle and sheep for export. To maintain the livestock over the long winter, oats and turnips were cultivated in rotation with sown grass, some of which was conserved as hay, and a smaller acreage of corn (bere) was also grown for human consumption. The introduction of new seeds, especially wild white clover (which came into common use in the 1920s), made a significant improvement in the quality of pasture. More cattle could be kept on the same acreage and the traditional five year rotation could be extended to six or even seven years, with the land lying longer in grass. There was no major change in the basic system, however, until the 1960s and it was still extremely labour-intensive.

Even when tractors replaced horses, the harvesting of oats and bere with the traditional methods of cutting with a binder, stooking, leading, stacking and threshing still demanded a huge amount of man hours. Neeps (turnips or swedes), the humble root which revolutionised British agriculture, obdurately resisted mechanisation and always had to be hoed and harvested by hand. One sight which remained unchanged at Holland from the 1860s until the 1960s was the line of men singling neeps!

While farming practices remained labour-intensive for the first half of the 20th century, labour was neither as plentiful nor as cheap as it had been. Inevitably the war had caused a shortage of labour and in 1917 minimum wages for farm servants were introduced for the first time in Lloyd George's Corn Production Act.[9] Orkney employers were outraged by a minimum rate of 37s a week which was far higher than the normal wage in the county. (The Agricultural Wages Act of 1937 would lay down the same basic rate 20 years later!) The break-up of the large estates meant that there were no longer "big" landlords who could afford to employ a large labour force, especially at fixed wages. Inevitably farmers attempted to cut their rising wages bill by mechanising their farms.

Among the debates organised by the Orkney Agricultural Discussion Society in the 1930s, cogent and emotive arguments for and against the replacement of the horse by the tractor must reflect many a heated public bar or farmhouse kitchen debate. In 1931 Charles Hourston was confident that "there need be no fear of serious replacement of the horse in agriculture by the tractor" and his passionate plea for a world in which beauty and sound economic sense paced side by side in gleaming harness resounds out of the pages of the society's journal. With some percipience, Hourston nailed the causes of the depression to the over-supply of agricultural produce resulting from the huge-scale mechanisation of farming, especially in America, but there is a sense that his cause, however good his arguments in the debating room, had already been lost on Orkney farms. His opponent from the West Mainland had used a tractor for 11 years and found that "one man works the plough and tractor and is able to plough as much ground as four men and eight horses with single ploughs". It was the argument that tractors would cut the cost of wages "which a heavy one in these times of depression" that would have most influence.[10]

Mechanisation did not happen rapidly or evenly in Orkney, however. Some of the large farms may have been mechanising in the 1920s but the great majority of farms

Men on the east banks of Papay burning kelp using a straw "flakkie' to fan the fire. Kelp making (for the production of iodine) was an arduous and unpleasant task but it was still providing an important addition to the farm income during the depression between the two world wars. Kelp was made on Papay until the early 1930s, when demand finally ceased altogether.

were now very small owner-occupied units, which could not afford large investments in machinery. Although tractors, especially the "little grey Fergie", became commonplace after the Second World War, (there were 80 in Westray by 1950)[11], many farms were still horse-worked until the 1960s.

Brown bred Clydesdales and travelled his stallions in Westray. It can be imagined that he had little enthusiasm for replacing his horses with machines, and it was 1938 before the folk of Papay would come running to the South-West Toun to see Abby Brown ploughing with a Ferguson. The island's first tractor was a cumbersome machine with iron spikes rather than tyres on its wheels, so sacks had to be laid across the road to enable it to get from one field to another. By 1950 there were two second-hand tractors, a Farmall International and an Allis Chalmers, with rubber tyres (but still used with iron spikes for ploughing) and these were succeeded by first petrol/paraffin and then diesel-engined Fergusons. It was some time, however, before any tractor could compete with the deeply ingrained prejudice of men who had worked with horses all their lives. John Scott, a young man when he took over the tenancy, was quite willing to send tractors to Holland but his manager strenuously defended the farm against mechanisation.

John Hourston, who became Scott's manager in 1941, never believed that tractors could work as well as horses and viewed their incursion into the farm with the deepest suspicion. Against his better judgement, tractors were gradually and reluctantly allowed to perform certain tasks, such as cutting the crop and harrowing, but he always insisted on sowing the neeps with a horse and horses were used for ploughing long after most other tasks were performed by tractor - on stony fields the cast-iron plough socks were broken less quickly if drawn by a horse!

In the 10 or 20 years after the war there was a steady and inexorable disappearance of both men and horses from the land. Until the war there were still five pairs of horses and 10 men (including a blacksmith) employed full-time at Holland, and virtually every able-bodied man and boy on the island was recruited for hay-making and the hairst. By 1950 the number of horses had dropped to five and the full-time servants to six. In the mid 1960s a couple of men left, lured by the opportunity to earn higher wages working on the construction of the new pier, and the last horses were sold. By the time that John Hourston and John Rendall took over the farm in 1967 they were running it with a total staff of three and no horses at all. The older John was officially "retired" but grandson Neil was working full-time at Holland from 1970 and soon the farm was managed by the family alone, with casual labour employed only at hay-time and hairst.

The Mill Tramp *(Inga Hourston)*

X

Of Beasts and Men

The winter lift is glintan doun
Wi tullimentan stars besprent,
As were the very heavens abune
Glean gyte wi' frosty merriment,
Their lowan e'en are taaken tent
O' chiels like Mansie o' the Bu'
Whase days upon the land are spent
Ruggan wi' Taurus and the Pleugh
Robert Rendall, "Celestial Kinsmen"

Whatever Holland's changes of fortune, or the great political and economic changes in the country, it can be imagined that the daily routine of farm servants and beasts changed remarkably little. The annual cycle of work that John Rendall experienced at Holland in the 1950s and early '60s would have been much the same in the previous decades, and very similar on any of the larger Orkney farms.

When he first came to work full-time at Holland in 1951 he was one of "four Johnnies" among the six servants. John Hourston managed the farm in Scott's absence; Johnno (John Rendall) and his son John Henry lived on the farm, and John Rendall, Jock Hume and his brother Robbie Hume all lived with their families in the New Hooses. When there were a number of servants employed on every large farm, each had his specialised area of responsibility and there was a strict ladder of promotion. A lad might start, as John Hourston did, as fourth or fifth horseman and finally work his way up the hierarchy to become first horseman and finally foreman. As manager John Hourston had overall responsibility, but he took a share in every job and did all the work with the pigs. He would be up first to feed the horses at six o'clock and would supper them and groom them at eight or nine at night. John and Robbie and John Henry were the horsemen and also worked with the tractors, while Johnno and Jock looked after the cattle.

The standard working day was nine hours long. Winter and summer farm servants worked from seven o'clock until 11 in the mornings, and from one o'clock until six at night. No unnecessary work would be undertaken on Sundays, but as long as the cattle were indoors there was very little respite even then. The 1937 Agricultural Wages Act had introduced a slightly more liberal regime, with work stopping at half-past five for three months in the winter, a half-day on Saturdays and one Sunday off every three weeks for the cattlemen. This last arrangement did not find much favour with the horsemen who had to look after the cattle in their stead! In early August, during the lull between singling neeps and haymaking and the beginning of the hairst, the men took a fortnight's holiday, which invariably centred on the County Show (the modern replacement for the Lammas Fair of the past), and a week in Kirkwall, "the Toun".

The Hourston family outside the grieve's house in the late 1940s. Left to right, Maggie, John and Annie Jean.

In 1951 a Holland servant's wages were £3 a week, after deductions had been made for his allowance of tatties, meal and milk from the farm. Exactly as in the 19th century, a few cows were handmilked and each servant was entitled to "one sweet pint of milk a day", (this was the Scotch pint, or half a gallon), plus an annual allowance of beremeal and oatmeal, drills of tatties (both of these would feed the servant's hens as well as his family) and sometimes coal. In contrast to the 19th century, the labourers' wages (and the value of the commodities) were fixed by the Agricultural Wages Act and the wages steadily rising.

The year revolved - as it still does - around the care of the beef cattle which for the last 150 years have been the main produce of Holland. For many generations the only cattle kept were the black or blue-grey type. Black polled and shorthorn bulls were present at the 1889 and the 1922 displenish sales and Brown sought out high-quality animals, paying the unheard-of price of 100 guineas for an Aberdeen Angus bull in the 1920s. Throughout Scott's tenancy there was always at least one Angus bull and a horned Shorthorn on the farm and it was not until the early 1960s that experiment was made with breeds other than Shorthorns or Blacks, with the introduction of Hereford bulls. The Hereford cross beast was thought to fatten more quickly than traditional types and for some years was extremely popular throughout the country until it was displaced by the fashion for the much larger and faster-maturing Continental breeds.

The cattle have to be housed indoors for at least six months each winter and until 1974 they were all tied in stalls and had to be fed and cleaned out manually. The kye's byre built in 1899 housed only 26 milking cows but, besides rearing their progeny,

Shipping cattle at the Kirkwall pier c. 1930. Cattle and horses had to be lifted aboard by crane on the North Isles boats and the larger ferries that took them south to Aberdeen from Mainland Orkney. Cattle were loaded in this undignified manner at the old pier in Papay when the tide did not suit the use of a gangplank.

(Orkney Library Photographic Archive)

Holland tended to buy in weaned calves from all the smaller farms which could not over-winter them, and sell them fattened. The shortage of feed during the First World War and for some time afterwards ensured that all Orkney farms exported their cattle as young beasts, but gradually between the wars the pendulum swung to fattening again and Holland was certainly selling fat cattle into the mid 1950s - often directly to the Ministry of Food, which bought livestock at a fixed price per hundredweight. With cattle maturing more slowly than they do today (as the result of selective breeding and better feeding), this meant keeping them until they were about three years old so there were a large number of young beasts on the farm. Since the last war the direction of government subsidy has become the crucial factor in determining farming policy, and from the 1950s it was geared to encourage the production of store cattle for fattening on mainland Scotland. Department of Agriculture grants were paid on cows and calves so feeding stirks became less profitable than keeping more cows. Scott raised the number of cows at Holland to 70, and every available building was converted into a byre to accommodate them.

The cattlemen divided responsibility for the 160 or so animals between them. Johnno looked after the west byres: 24 feeding beasts (nearly fat) in the upper byre, 26

"Steamer Day" in the 1950s. The ss *Earl Thorfinn* is loading at the old pier in Papay. Note the egg boxes in the forreground and the kelp stores at the rear

(Orkney Library Photographic Archive)

less forward in the middle byre and a bull and 11 heifers in the lower byre. In Jock's domain were the cows and their calves and a bull in the kye's byre, 22 older calves in the adjoining calfie byre and 24 older still in the oxy byre. The young calves were tied along the wall behind their mothers in the kye's byre, so twice a day they had to be untied to feed and then recaptured. It was a skilful job to drag each calf from its mother at exactly the right moment and re-tether it. If left too long, 26 black calves would be careering all over the byre!

Every day the byres had to be cleaned with shovel and wheelbarrow, and straw, oats, neeps and hay carried to the stalls. There was no piped water until 1955 so the cattle had to be loosed and taken to the quarry for a drink daily. Sometimes, when they were eating plenty of neeps, the feeding cattle did not require much water and might be only taken to the quarry three times in the week, but the milking cattle were always taken every day. They were so familiar with their routine that they would walk back into their own stalls to be bound, but the whole process still took two to three hours. When the weather was too bad to let the cattle out, pails of water had to be carried to them. It would take two hours to do the 31 trips back and forth with two pails between the west byres - which did not get piped water until 1967 - and the trough outside the stable. In the winter of 1947 it snowed from mid January to mid March and the quarry was frozen over so solidly that the men had to take all the cattle the whole way down to the loch to drink, a half-mile journey each way.

In April or early May the cattle could finally be let out to grass. There were far fewer dykes on the steading in the 1950s than at present, and so a great many more opportunities for chaos when the excited beasts were released from their stalls. There was no dyke between the byres and the road or the track to the Links, and at their first taste of freedom the calves were apt to disappear in every direction unless each one was dragged to the park on a rope. (In 1967 the dyke was taken down between Housen and Back o' th' Millers to make a bigger airfield for the new plane service, and John Rendall had the stones brought to Holland and built the dykes enclosing "the square" which now curb bovine high spirits and make life considerably easier.)

The summer of 1955 was memorable at Holland for the disastrous discovery of tuberculosis in the herd. The government had introduced a TB Eradication Scheme and all herds were being compulsorily tested. (The programme had started with the south of England and cleared the country northward to the border, it then jumped to Shetland and worked southward. In this way Shetland and Orkney farmers were able to continue selling their cows and young beasts to farms in Scotland which had not yet been tested). TB was found in the Holland cattle and so throughout that summer the whole herd had to be brought into the byre twice every six weeks for the test. As more and more cows tested positive the entire milking herd had to be culled. John Scott sent over replacements from his farm in Harray and also more fattening beasts, and although the cattle were all outside a number of these also went down with the disease. John Rendall remembers spending all summer disinfecting the byre walls with a flame-gun and picking out the seams and re-cementing them. Fortunately, Papay avoided the serious outbreak of foot and mouth disease which affected Orkney in 1959 and 1960.

Holland kept the only bulls on the island. A small government subsidy was paid to farmers who allowed their bulls to be used by the crofters in their district. Once a year John Hourston made the round of the island collecting a service fee of 10s for every cow brought to Holland's bull. This delicate matter was considered to be an entirely masculine domain. If a woman brought her cow to the farm, she disappeared into the house for a cup of tea with the womenfolk, while the men attended to the bringing together of cow and bull. The cattleman competed for this responsibility as the man who let the bull out was entitled to a fee: 6d in the 1940s had risen to 1s by the 1950s.

Neeps, hay and hairst, the securing of winter fodder, dominated the work all the summer months while the cattle were outside. Until the mid '60s the farm was always sown with 80 acres of oats and 40 acres of neeps every year, so the fields were combined to make six approximately 40 acre units: (the South-West Toun and five acres of the May, Housen and North Park, Eastside and Poultie, Lening with Quarry Park and Mid Quival, Vanglee with Bolispel and Back o' th' Millers, the May and the North-West Toun) and these were cultivated in a strict six year rotation. The first year they were ploughed and sown with oats. This was lea oats, followed by a year in turnips. The third year oats was sown again, undersown with grass, and this was known as clean land. The field then stayed in grass for the next three years before the cycle was repeated.

Artificial fertiliser was put on all the crop and neep fields, though not often on the grass, and until the arrival of a manure sower in 1955 it all had to be sown by hand. It arrived at the farm in two-hundredweight sacks of sulphate of ammonia and superphosphate which had to be tipped on to the floor of the barn, mixed together with

This picture was taken at Skaill on Westray but the long line of labourers singling neeps (turnips) would have been a familiar sight on a summer day on any large farm between the 1860s and the 1960s. *(Orkney Library Photographic Archive)*

a shovel, rebagged and lifted on to a float. John Hourston would drive the horse-drawn float, while another man sat on the back broadcasting the highly abrasive pellets. (A contributor to the Orkney Agricultural Discussion Society had commented in 1930 that "the introduction of the manure sower has dispensed with one of the most unpleasant of farm jobs")!

The lea was ploughed in the autumn and the neep land in spring for sowing with oats in April. A broadcasting machine was used for sowing the white oats but it did not work with the rougher grains of black oats and certain fields (such as Bolispel) were always regarded as unfit for growing white oats so they had to be sown by hand. A man could sow 10 acres in an afternoon, broadcasting with both hands from a sowing sheet tied at his waist. The hairst started in the last days of August or early September and usually lasted two months, only finishing in early November. Cutting with the three horse binder was a slow business. The crop was almost invariably lodged by the wind and had to be cut in one direction (so that the ears fell first on the binder). With the binder working only as it drove up the field it could take a week to cut one field. Initially the binder was assisted by two teams of three men, one with a scythe and two lifting sheaves, to clear roads around the field to allow the machine a clear space to work in, but by the mid 1960s the labour force was not large enough to allow the luxury of scythe teams and the binder had to be driven across the standing crop at the start of each field.

After cutting, the sheaves were stooked in groups of six and left in the field to dry and ripen. A gale of wind could easily scatter the carefully stooked sheaves and the laborious process had to start all over again. When the sheaves were thought to be dry enough and the weather was reasonable, leading began. One team of men loaded the stooks in the field, one or two men pitchforking the sheaves on to a trailer where another man carefully built them into a high and stable load. In the stackyard another team of two men built each load into a stack, first laying the stone stack-steethes into a circular foundation, 16 feet in diameter. A good crop would fill the Holland yard with 40 stacks and building them was a skilful operation. Photographs of the annual stackbuilding competitions held in Orkney show the pride in a perfectly built stack.

As the straw and oats were needed during the winter the stacks were dismantled, built again on a trailer and taken to the barn for threshing. In their final manhandling, the sheaves were pitchforked into the sheaf loft and fed into the diesel engine-driven threshing mill. The operation of the mill separated grain and straw, the latter falling into a buncher which tied it into bundles ready for feeding. The grain was cleaned from the chaff and both fell to the ground floor of the barn where the oats was bagged and carried to the manual hoist which lifted the sacks to the grain loft on the upper floor. The best of the oats would be stored here for seed while most of it was bruised for cattle feed, the bruiser being part of the mill and operated at the same time as threshing. The heavy work of moving the sacks of oats in the barn would be done when the men first started work at seven o'clock in the morning, when it was too dark to work outside. In 1954 the mill was modernised with an elevator that carried the grain back up to the sheaf loft and past fanners that blew it down the conveyor that ran the length of the 70 foot grain loft. The mill was in use until 1992, although for the last few years of its working life only a few acres of crop were grown at Holland.

Farm servants had always been paid an annual allowance of oatmeal (and beremeal while it was grown on the farm) as part of their wages. After milling the meal was stored in the meal loft and in the huge girnels below and weighed out to the servants on a massive iron balance, but around the turn of the century both the watermill and the windmill in Papay ceased to function so every winter a portion of Holland's crop had to be sent away by steamer to the nearest mill. At one time all the Papay farms would take their grain to the large Trenabie watermill in Pierowall, sailing across to Westray in small boats when the weather was fine, but when it closed around 1960 the oats had to be sent to the mill in Stronsay. The meal came back in boll (140lb) sacks which were distributed to all who worked on the farm. The miller was not paid in cash but took a multure, or fixed portion of the meal, as payment for his work. The last occasion that grain was sent away to be milled was in 1968 and the Stronsay mill closed down shortly afterwards.

Neeps were sown in late May and all through July the workforce were kept busy singling the crop. It was enormously demanding on labour but it fell in a quiet time, for the hay was made later then than now and not mown until August. Throughout the winter the neeps were harvested by hand and taken to the turnip sheds adjoining the byres, where every day a ration would be chopped to feed the cattle.

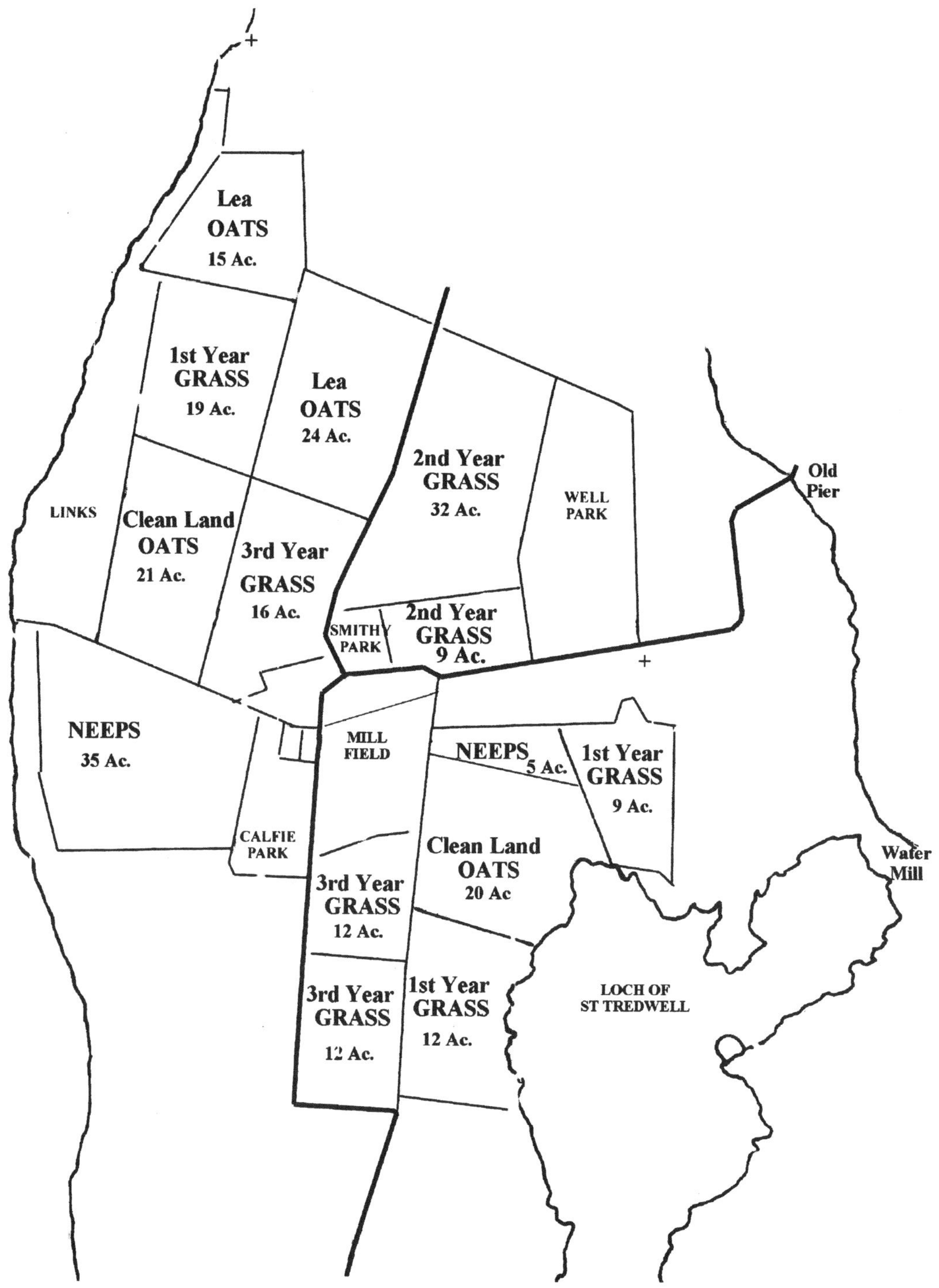

Plan of Holland Farm in 1950. The fields were cultivated in a six year rotation: oats, neeps, oats, then three years in grass.

Straw, bruised oats and neeps was the diet of the older cattle, but the calves were always given hay. When the full acreage of crop was grown, about 10 to 20 acres of hay sufficed, but as less crop was cultivated this was increased to 30 or 35 acres and hay-making was almost entirely a manual process. The grass was cut by tractor-drawn reaper, but then the swathes were turned by hoe until dry enough to rake into coles. When sufficiently cured and dry, the coles were pitchforked on to a trailer and taken to the haybarn. Machinery arrived earlier at some of the more progressive of the smaller farms. John remembers turning the hay with a hoe up and down the long rows of the 30 acre field Housen in 1959, when the men of Whitehow brought their new hay-turner to finish the job at miraculous speed. In the early '60s Tommo o' Whitehow brought his baler to Holland, and in 1967 Holland shared the purchase of their first baler with Mayback and the Links. In the first years of baling each bale had to be picked up individually and stacked ready for loading on to the trailer, so the next welcome invention for speeding up this process was the bale sledge, which enabled 10 bales to be collected behind the baler and dropped off together. When there were 7,000 to 10,000 bales to bring home and stack in the barn, the work needed as many energetic extra people as could be found.

There were, then as now, busy times of year with the sheep flock. The breed of sheep most popular among the Orkney "Improvers" was the half-bred, or Cheviot/Leicester cross, and Thomas Traill introduced these to Holland in the middle of the last century. Half-bred ewes were sold in the 1889 displenish sale, but were reintroduced to the farm and their descendants have been here ever since. Besides the "big sheep" (crossed with Suffolk and Texel rams for fat lamb production) Holland has always pastured a flock of about 100 native sheep on the Holm. The "holmies" were probably originally identical to the North Ronaldsay sheep, but they have repeatedly been crossed with Shetland rams in order to improve the quality of their wool, and so are mostly white and slightly larger than the pure Orkney natives. Unlike some of the smaller holms such as Aikerness, which are almost drowned at high tide and have nothing but seaweed for the sheep to eat, the Papay Holm is relatively luxurious with over 40 acres of pasture. The salt-soaked grass is poor, however, and at each low tide the sheep are foraging for ware on the rocky shore.

Holmies are less a domesticated sheep than a wild animal that is occasionally hunted, and their hunting is one activity that has changed little over the past decades. To survive and raise lambs on their bleak and shelterless island they have to be wise and wily; consequently they disdain to flock together as domestic sheep do when gathered but scatter in all directions to the steep craigs and slippery rocks where humans struggle to follow. Gathering is therefore a challenge and the annual round-up or "Holmie Day" is a cheerful event that still involves every able-bodied person on the island. This takes place in July, on a date determined by the tide and expectation of fair weather. When the word goes round from Holland all other jobs are abandoned and every available small boat launched. The strategy depends on the use of long nets handmade from baling string, which are held taut between every pair of gatherers so that they can make a (theoretically) impenetrable wall right across the island from shore to shore. In practice, as the sheep find themselves driven nearer the fank they panic and break back and, despite desperate running and hallooing on the part of their

As farm servant, manager and, finally owner, John Hourston (1902-79) lived at Holland for 60 years.

pursuers, escape under or over or through the nets. This exhausting process is repeated until a reasonable quorum is gathered into the fank beside the old "horsie hoose".

In the past the gatherers would spend the whole day on the Holm, making a fire to brew their tea at midday. The north end flock was driven into the steep-sided "Sheepie Geo" and from there into a stone fank. The south end flock were penned with a temporary wire fence on to the south cruive, and then caught in a small house. The sheep were hand-clipped, dipped and dosed; the lambs castrated; the fleeces rolled and stowed in wool-sacks and the "sheepies", or one-year-old wethers, carried down to the boats for fattening on the farm to fulfil their function as the island mutton supply. Nowadays there are several fences across the island so that it can be gathered in sections and the job is done much more quickly even with the depleted numbers of people available, but the "sheep-processing" is much the same. For the rest of the year the holmies live entirely undisturbed, the rams being taken across in the dinghy at the end of November and retrieved whenever the weather permits after the new year. Holmie Day ends with coming home on boats full of people and sheep and woolsacks to a large tea spread out in Holland's loft. It is one of the year's highlights, a day which in the memory is always one of sunshine and laughter, and in which the smells of salmon sandwiches and sheepdip are inextricably commingled.

Holland's economy in the past was more diverse than at present. Besides the cattle and sheep, both poultry and pigs played an extremely important role. Throughout the first half of this century the Orkney economy depended to an extraordinary degree on egg production. Orkney was exporting eggs from the early 19th century (five 30-dozen boxes went out of the county in 1805) and the value and quantity rose steadily until by 1870 700,000 dozen eggs were exported, worth £27,000.[1] Poultry became a major industry in the 1880s when the low prices for grain made it more economic to use it on the farm than export it. In 1914 egg exports reached 19 million, the very high war-time prices pushing their value to £357,148, and hen-houses became a dominant feature of the Orkney landscape.[2] Although prices fell back after the war, hens remained very profitable. The Department of Agriculture gave encouragement to poultry breeding and the number of fowls in the county continued to rise to about half a million in 1939, when Scarth and Watt reported that "the annual value of the egg exports nearly equals the combined value of that for cattle, horses, sheep and pig exports". [3] By 1949 Orkney's annual egg exports were worth £750,000.

In Papay the height of the "egg boom" was certainly the war years, when John Scott was keeping hens in almost every field of Holland and poultry numbers on the island reached a staggering 11,228 in the 1945 census! [4] Every farm servant kept hens; there was a row of hen-houses at the back of the New Houses, and keen competition to obtain the most eggs. It was a very significant but almost cashless economy. The allowance of meal and drills of tatties which the servant was paid as part of his wage supplied hen feed, and the eggs were traded for other groceries with the local merchant. The terrible gales of 1952 blew hundreds of the wooden hen-houses out to sea and numbers on Papay fell considerably, but the poultry industry in Orkney as a whole recovered from this disaster and egg exports reached a zenith of a staggering 5,599 tons in 1959.[5] However, by this time competition from large-scale intensive producers in the south were causing egg prices to fall (from 3s 7d a dozen in 1955, for example, to only 2s 6d ten years later) and the high costs of imported feed so eroded profits that egg exports declined steadily throughout the 1960s.

Pigs were always present on the island in small numbers, but they had their heyday at Holland in the 1950s, in a brief era of high prices which saw as many as 16,000 pigs exported from Orkney in 1954.[6] Pigs were kept in every building at Holland that could be spared - the old bothy, the mill tramp, as well as the pig-houses in the back yard and Patties Park. Holland kept breeding sows and boars and most of the progeny were sold as young pigs to the smaller farms on Papay and Westray, to be fattened on their excess milk and tatties. In the mid '50s pig prices declined as abruptly as they had risen, but remained profitable enough to be bred at Holland until 1967.

Another subsidiary farm income in these years came from the export of rabbits. In Westray in 1950 it was reported that "Rabbits are caught in thousands and sent to game dealers in the south. During the season it is sometimes impossible to find a corner of the post office counter at which to do business owing to the piled bundle of rabbits awaiting despatch by the mail boat".[7] Unlike the farmed livestock, rabbits seemed to have remained constantly both plentiful and profitable from Lord Henry Sinclair's time until recent years. They were still a small sideline at Holland until undercut by the import of Chinese rabbits into Orkney in 1988.

In the Second World War years farming had received a tremendous boost from the demand for foodstuffs such as milk, potatoes and eggs from the huge numbers of armed forces personnel that were stationed in the islands. The war was so beneficial to Orkney's economy that peace appears to have been oddly little celebrated, (the news of VE Day appears only in a page three column of the local newspaper!) An onlooker reported wryly in *The Orcadian* of May 10, 1945, on the scene in the Kirkwall Auction Mart where "a packed assembly of farmers, crofters, dealers and butchers carried on with their business - no halt of any kind occurring when the end-of-fighting word came through". Under the portraits of Churchill and caricatures of Hitler "the quick-fire acceptance of bids for young heifers prevailed as the item of major interest and casual asides about the war were heard occasionally between deals."

When the military left, farming dropped again into the doldrums, and in the 20 years or so after the war Holland shared problems that were common to all Orkney farms, but especially acute in the North Isles. Wages had risen steeply during the war (the minimum wage for a cattleman, for example, had more than doubled between 1940 and 1945) and the rise in the cost of living and of all agricultural necessities was far outstripping the slow increase in the price of agricultural produce. Between 1951 and 1964 cattle prices rose only 60 per cent of the rise in the cost of living, pig and sheep prices stayed stationary, and at the same time transport costs were soaring at the rate of 8 per cent per annum.[8]

All the feed and fertiliser that Orkney farmers needed had to be shipped into the islands from Aberdeen; all their livestock had to be shipped out. With no facility for slaughtering and exporting beef, the cattle had to be sent south on the hoof and so producers were entirely dependent on the vagaries of mainland markets. North Isles farms were especially vulnerable, as freight charges to and from the isles added as much as 40 per cent to the Aberdeen-Kirkwall costs. According to the *Orkney Farming Survey* of 1966, "Apart from climate, freight costs represent the greatest handicap facing Orkney agriculture at the present time . . . particularly in the North Isles".[9] If the dealers at Kirkwall Mart were paying low prices for stock it was seldom worth while to pay the heavy freights on shipping sheep and cattle home again, and make the animals endure another seven- to nine-hour journey on the steamer's twice-weekly tour of the isles.

In these circumstances it was very hard for any Orkney farm to raise the capital for investment in improvements. Agricultural advisors might recommend modernised buildings or equipment, but as long as stock prices remained low it was simply too hard to find the spare cash. Most Orkney farms were still small. The average size in 1951 was only 34 acres and by 1960 there were still many, especially in the North Isles, under 10 acres. Despite a steady amalgamation of farms as small units found themselves unviable, even by 1969 45 per cent contained less than 10 cows.[10] Larger farms like Holland were much more economic, but they were struggling with the shortage and cost of labour.

"Holmie Day" picnic in the 1940s.

Although farm wages had increased dramatically, they were still not keeping pace with the wages that men could earn elsewhere, and so farm servants were not only hard to pay out of the farm income but hard to find. This was particularly true in small islands like Papay where the population nose-dived from the time of the war, (declining 49 per cent between 1951 and 1981).[11] There was every incentive to find a system of husbandry that was less labour-intensive than the traditional one, and farmers were becoming increasingly aware that by switching from grain to intensive grass production their farm could carry 50 per cent more stock with less than a quarter of the man-hours of labour. Orkney started to undergo its "green revolution".

Farm land that had formerly been sown with oats and neeps was now sown only with grass, grown with large applications of fertiliser for heavy crops. Between 1959 and 1969 the area of oats in Orkney fell from 27,052 to 17,159 acres, neeps from 5,331 to 1,481, but in the same time the acreage of grass for mowing almost doubled and silage increased by 250 per cent, though it was still not as important as hay.[12] All over Orkney the same trends were evident; crops declined but greater numbers of cattle and sheep were exported from the islands every year. Farms grew larger as they absorbed smaller ones but the number of people employed in farming dropped steadily. The familiar patchwork of arable fields was replaced by continuous grassland.

These changes tended to happen a little later in the islands than on the Orkney Mainland, but everywhere farms were being forced in the same direction in order to survive with a fraction of their former manpower. Holland's acres of oats and neeps were already declining when John Scott gave up the tenancy, and the farm crossed another watershed in its own history at a time when all Orkney was undergoing a major transformation of its agriculture and its landscape.

The West Barn *(Inga Hourston)*

XI

On Fortune's Wheel

No meet honour hath the plough. The fields, their husbandmen led away, rot in neglect
Virgil, *The Georgics*

In 1967 Holland was again in the hands of owner-occupiers after almost 80 years of tenancies and Orkney farming was entering a new era. A radical break was being made with the traditional system of husbandry, livestock prices were rising and a time of rapid modernisation and increasing prosperity lay ahead. For the first time in 100 years there was major investment in Holland.

An analysis of post-war Orkney farming published in 1966 concluded that the only way forward for Orkney's farmers was to concentrate on intensive grassland farming, rather than cereals, and to finish and slaughter cattle in Orkney.[1] The last suggestion, which represented "the most radical change over current practice and one presenting the greatest challenge" could not be carried out until the abattoir was built in Kirkwall in 1981, but throughout the 1960s and '70s Orkney farmers were heeding the advice to turn their farms into grassland.

These developments had significant, and contentious, effects on the Orkney landscape. Most obviously, the yellow-and-brown patchwork of arable farms divided into grain crop, root crop and grass disappeared into a sea of uniform green. Agricultural subsidies also encouraged a huge increase in the numbers of sheep in the county and consequently a far greater pressure on pasture land. The use of wild white clover from the 1920s onward had so improved the inbye land that it could support a farm's livestock, and consequently the hill grazing was little used for half a century and its natural heath vegetation allowed to flourish. This situation changed about 1980 with growing numbers of sheep grazing the hill and the adjoining marginal land. Subsidies also encouraged widespread reclamation of moorland and marshland by draining and applying lime and basic slag to create improved grassland. Not only was much of Orkney's hitherto natural landscape transformed by agriculture, but these changes had disastrous effects on the wildlife it had supported. Bird populations that had relied on stubble fields as winter feeding grounds, for example, lost this resource as grain gave way to grass, and others lost their hunting or nesting territories as moorland and marsh were swallowed in the advancing tide of manicured green fields. This process co-inciding with a new increase of interest in the conservation of the environment, backed by government support from a different direction, brought the two issues into a new and sometimes acrimonious conflict.

At Holland the 80 acres of oats had fallen to 30 acres by 1979 and the 40 acres of neeps dwindled to a fraction of an acre. Besides the crop, about 30 acres of hay was grown for winter keep, but in the disastrously wet summer of that year hay-making was virtually impossible and the grass was made into silage. This was not the first experiment with silage at Holland but when it was previously attempted in the 1940s the effort of cutting out the compacted material with a spade was found so laborious that it was abandoned. The technique of silage-making (in which grass is preserved by a self-pickling process when it is tightly compressed), was introduced into the country from America around 1880 and in the 1920s a number of Orkney farms were building concrete or wooden silage towers. Silage has the beguiling advantage over hay that it can be made when the grass is damp and does not require the settled dry weather that is not a guaranteed feature of the Orkney summer, but it took a long time to become generally popular as its making required expensive machinery. While hay could be made on the smallest farm with only the family labour force and simple tools, the 1920s silo was reckoned to take 10 or 12 men to fill - two with a reaper, three with carts, two fillers, two packers and three to keep the tractor-driven cutter and blower going!.[2] While the machinery had been invented for blowing the chopped grass *into* the silo, it would be a long time before one appeared that could efficiently get it *out*, and although silage acres increased in Orkney during the 1960s it was the next decade before improved harvesters and mechanised cutters would make the crop more popular than hay.

In 1979 the silage still had to be cut out with a spade, but by the next year the first tractor-driven silage cutter had arrived and the process of conserving winter keep was revolutionised. With a new silo it was possible to make the bulk of the grass crop into silage, mowing just a few acres for hay (mainly for the calves). Over the years more modern forage harvesters have speeded up the silage-making process until the winter keep for twice the number of cattle kept in the 1970s is now made in a fraction of the time. Silage has replaced the hairst as the most labour-intensive event of the year, since it requires a team of five men operating at one time (one mowing, one on the harvester, two carting and one packing in the pit), but whereas the hairst took months of labour, and hay weeks, 100-120 acres of silage can now be made in four or five days. In 1996 the next stage in silage equipment, a round baler, was purchased co-operatively by the newly-formed Papay Machinery Group. The invention of efficient silage machinery seems to have been the most significant single factor in the late 20th century "agricultural revolution".

John Hourston's reservations about mechanisation were not passed down his family and the last couple of decades have seen ever-larger tractors arrive at Holland, but where once the tractor could be accused of displacing people and creating rural unemployment, by the late 20th century it had become essential for farmers to seek more sophisticated machinery so that their farm could be managed by the very small number of people available. For the same reason, survival depended on modernising steadings which were designed for a system of husbandry that depended on a plentiful supply of cheap labour. At Holland, with improving stock prices and much thrift, profits were coming out of the farm again and were immediately ploughed back into it as the work of creating a practical late 20th-century farm went ahead.

In 1970 a generator was installed and the byres were lit by electricity for the first time, an innovation that must have made an enormous difference to the winter work. (The house had to wait another couple of years for this amenity, as Department of

John o' Holland (John Rendall), owner of Holland Farm, which he has worked for over 50 years.

Agriculture grant was only available for lighting plants for steadings. Mains electricity was brought to the island by underwater cable 10 years later.) Throughout the 1970s parts of the steading were renovated or rebuilt to render the task of looking after the cattle in winter less laborious for a workforce of only two or three men. Gradually the old fashioned tied byres were replaced with loose byres. In 1974 the west byres were enlarged as a cubicle byre and feeding shed for 46 cows and for the first time a tractor-scraper could replace the wheelbarrow and shovel for cleaning out! In 1976 there was a Dutch barn and by the 1980s the farm was able to undertake even more ambitious projects. A large silo in 1982 was followed in 1984/85 by a slatted floor byre, housing 120-140 cattle and dispensing with the daily cleaning routine altogether.

Machinery and modern buildings have enormously reduced the strenuous physical labour of the past, but recent years have seen other demands made on the farmer. Skills with livestock and machinery or a philosophical attitude to going outside late on a wet night to calve a cow are no longer enough unless the farmer also has the ability to double-up as a civil servant and cope with a vast and ever-increasing amount of paperwork. A lifetime's knowledge of beasts or crops will hardly avail the farmer of the future whose office does not bristle with the paraphernalia of modern technology and who is not as familiar with his computer as his grandfather was with a pitchfork.

When the Rendalls took over the stock in 1967 they could afford only 44 cows (valued at £60 each) with 25 calves (£30), but gradually the numbers built up again. The cows calved indoors during the winter and their progeny were sold in the autumn as weaned calves. Most of these would be bought by dealers and shipped to Aberdeen, and many thousands of young cattle still leave the islands every September and October for the markets of the south. When the new byre was completed in 1985 there was enough housing to keep 70 cows and their followers and by this time it was possible and profitable to sell fat beasts directly to the abattoir instead of sending them to dealers. The calves are born outside in spring and autumn and sold whenever they are ready for slaughter, at 18 months to two years old.

In 1983 Neil Rendall and neighbour Bobby Rendall trained in artificial insemination (AI) so that they could offer this service on the island. AI made an enormous difference to the quality of cattle everywhere, but especially in more remote areas where it enabled even the smallest farm to cross its cows with high-quality bulls, and the large continental breeds could be used without the expense of keeping these animals. Until 1996 there was no premium price paid for quality Angus cattle, and so continental cross calves were worth more as they finished at heavier weights. There was a brief period of experiment with crossing the cows with the whole gamut of new breeds available - Charolais, Limousin, Simmental, Romagnola, Blonde Acquitaine . . . but the Charolais quickly established itself as the most successful cross on the black cows. Charolais have remained popular in Orkney but for some years now only Angus bulls have been used at Holland and a pedigree herd was founded in 1991. In 1998 Neil Rendall was presented at Perth with the William Sclater perpetual trophy for the "highest standard of stock presented" to Aberdeen Angus Producers and in 2000 was judged runner-up in the Aberdeen Angus national "Herd of the Year" competition.

Hairst: Neil Rendall on the binder cutting the crop;

"stooking" sheaves;

and finally father, John, feeding sheaves from the elevator into the threshing mill (late 1980s).

Neil Rendall, right, receiving the William Sclater Perpetual Trophy for his pedigree AA stock at the Perth Bull Sales in 1998

During the last 30 years of the 20th century livestock prices fluctuated considerably but there is no doubt that for most Orkney farms the overall picture, until 1996, was one of increasing prosperity. During the 1970s the prices that Holland was receiving for its stock at the mart were rising steadily but fell at the end of the decade when a very wet summer in 1979 made it almost impossible to harvest winter keep and cattle that would have been over-wintered had to be sent south. The "very poor conditions facing farming in the period 1978-80"[3] then gave way to a decade of generally improving prices in the 1980s. Such a period of optimism, encouraging expansion and investment, inevitably received a check. Orkney's physical isolation was no protection against the effects of disease on world markets and in 1990 cattle prices slumped as a result of the first scare over bovine spongiform encepalopathy, or BSE. The disease hardly touched the islands but it caused shock-waves of depression in the auction mart. This crisis, however, did not last and prices improved again in the following years.

Throughout the 1980s and early '90s, good cattle and sheep prices were bringing prosperity to the farm and to the island. The beef produced on Orkney's incredibly lush summer pastures gained a reputation for high quality, and with so many other trades depending on farming (such as machinery, feed, seeds, construction), the huge numbers of beasts heading south every year brought wealth into the Orkney economy as a whole. This confident picture was shattered on March 20, 1996 when the Europe-wide ban on the import of British beef was announced, due to the alarming incidence of BSE in dairy herds. The revelation of the probable cause of transmission, the use of animal bonemeal in cattle feed, and the assumed connection between BSE-infected meat and the fatal human disease vCJD, Creuzfeldt-Jakob's disease, caused widespread panic. The public perception of animal welfare and food safety standards in British farming was severely damaged and there was a collapse in the demand for beef at home as well as the closure of all export markets.

Loading cattle at the new pier in Papay (completed in 1970).

The great majority of farms in Orkney (and Scotland) were unaffected by the disease itself but the effects of the crisis were both financially damaging and deeply demoralising. In an attempt to prevent contaminated animals entering the food chain the government introduced legislation condemning all cattle over 30 months old. Despairing farmers watched healthy beasts head for the incinerator and their prime cattle sell at the mart for £150 or £200 less than they had been worth the previous year. In 1997 sheep prices also collapsed and that winter the sale of beef on the bone was made illegal. Fury at this legislation drove even the placid and law-abiding Orkney farmers to an unprecedented mass demonstration in Broad Street in Kirkwall on the occasion of the Secretary of State for Scotland's visit to Orkney in December 1997.

By 1998 it was evident that it was not only beef farming that was in collapse, but the whole agricultural industry. The strength of sterling had made British produce hard to sell overseas, while at home it struggled to compete with cheaper imported food. Dairy and sheep, cereal and pig farmers were all suffering from the slump in prices. The very high costs of implementing the new hygiene regulations kept butcher's meat expensive to the consumer, while the producer received less and less. Further blows came unexpectedly. The profitable export trade in sheepskins to Russia, formerly worth £9 a sheep, collapsed with the Russian economy. Lamb prices plummeted; in the Orkney Auction Mart they averaged about half of their level 10 years previously while sheep farmers in the Highlands and Shetland could not sell their small lambs at all. The price of cattle continued to fall. And it rained: the wettest July and August followed the second wettest June in Orkney in 50 years. Hay and silage lay in sodden fields weeks after the usual time of harvest, tractors got bogged in mud in desperate attempts

Angus cattle in the slatted byre at Holland.

to rescue something of the ruined winter keep and green fields were reduced to a quagmire.

In 1999 the European Union lifted the beef ban (although France and some other countries continued to enforce it) and cattle prices improved slightly. The despairing mood of 1998 lifted a little also but no one could predict when (or if) farming and the meat industry would recover from the blow to consumer confidence and their markets. A solution to the more basic problem of world-wide overproduction remained as far away as ever. Throughout the country, farmers continued to be hit by low prices for their produce, steeply rising costs, cuts in government support and bureaucratic hailstorms of new regulations. As a result many abandoned farming and so rural areas have lost their population, their traditional economic basis and their social identity. In the year 2000, 39 per cent of the farms sold in Scotland were purchased by non-farmers,[4] and this national trend is reflected in Papay where the number of working farms halved during the 1990s. Between 1997 and 1998 the number of cows kept on the island dropped by 25 per cent, and arable land, so precious and so hard-won in the past, fell out of use.

BSE and its aftermath threw an immense cloud of despondency over everyone connected with agriculture in the late 1990s. No-one imagined that British farming would soon suffer the far worse calamity of the catastrophic epidemic of foot and mouth disease which broke out in February 2001 and over the following months devastated Cumbria, Devon and south-west Scotland in particular. While Orkney and other areas remain free of the disease, the entire country is still (at the end of 2001)

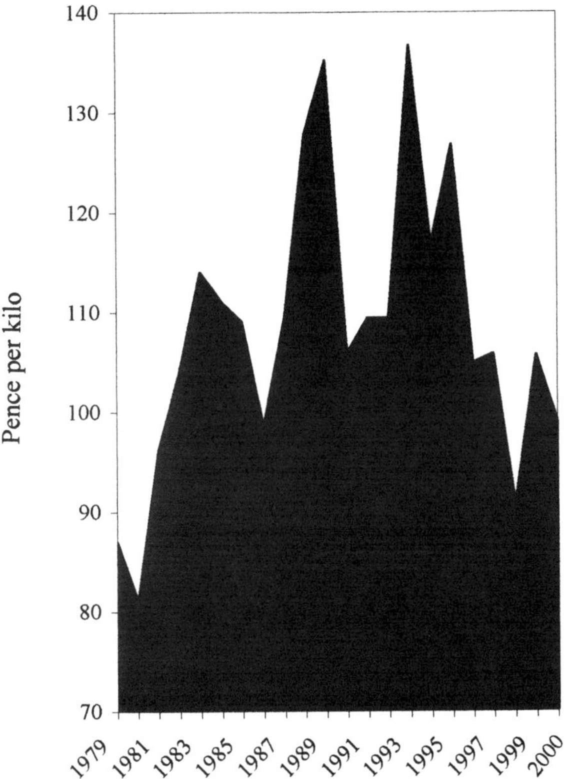

Cattle prices at Orkney Auction Mart, 1979 - 2000, based on the average price of steers sold at the first prime sale in July.

affected by the restriction on animal movements and consequently by the loss of export markets. With British farming heavily dependent on the export of its livestock, the effects of this loss can only be severe and far-reaching.

Previous periods of "depression", earlier in the 20th, the 19th or even the 15th centuries, are evidence that Orkney's agricultural economy has always been affected by trends in distant markets, on the continent or even world-wide, but a new factor was the extent of its dependence on direct political intervention, not only by the British government but by the European Union. Since the Second World War farm incomes have been increasingly dependent on subsidies. The corollary to this generous support is the vulnerability of farming to policies conceived, and changed, at a remote distance. The 1984 Orkney Economic Review found a "growing uncertainty in the industry" as a result of this insecurity and, by the end of the century, the uncertainty was a great deal more acute.

The European commitment to a reduction in subsidies and implementation of the General Agreement on Tariffs and Trade (GATT), which would remove agricultural protection and open world markets to free trade, offers a cheerless prospect to British farmers. It is unlikely that an unsubsidised British agricultural industry, with its high standards and high costs of production maintained by a web of regulations covering

"Holmie Day": going home with bulging woolsacks.

every aspect of livestock rearing, feeding, medication, welfare, transport, slaughter and processing, could compete against the cheaper products of countries unhampered by such strict legislation and enforcement.

Where does this leave Holland, or farming in Orkney in general, or the future of small islands, which in the past have always depended on agriculture for survival? The economics of modern farming dictates that, with a much smaller margin of profits per head of livestock to be expected in the future, farms must expand to survive and on this basis the acreage of Papay, for example, which once supported 50 families, would be appropriate to one or two large farms - or "agricultural units", perhaps. Where this course has been pursued it has maintained agricultural surpluses at the expense of drastic rural depopulation and environmental damage and for a small island community it offers no hope for the future at all.

There is also a growing lobby for farming and conservation interests to be seen as mutually supportive rather than incompatible and, with government will, areas rich in wildlife habitat like Orkney could benefit greatly from subsidies designed to promote environmentally-friendly farming rather than increased productivity. Agri-environment schemes have been vigorously promoted in other European countries, pre-eminently Finland, but are much more restricted in the United Kingdom as a whole which receives from the European Union less than half of the European average (per hectare of agricultural area) for agri-environment payments. These payments are considerably more restricted in Scotland than in England and Wales, but a change of policy in the Scottish Executive could open up new possibilities for farmers in "environmentally sensitive" areas.

Jocelyn Rendall and Cathie Gray clipping sheep on the Holm.

Rural depopulation is not, of course, a new nor an exclusively local problem. In 1517 it was so acute in England that the government set up a special commission to investigate the issue.[5] In 1955 (when there were at least twice as many people on Papay as at present), the North Isles Association was so concerned about the decline in numbers brought about by the "inconveniences" of their situation that a petition was sent to the Secretary of State (and a "most unsatisfactory" reply received!).[6] At the turn of the 21st century, schemes such as "Initiative on the Edge", in which Papay and Westray form one of the pilot "marginal areas" earmarked for regeneration, indicate government concern for the issues of rural decline and the initiative has attracted funding for projects for island development. Although this is welcome, the haemorrhage of people from the countryside is a phenomenon occurring all over Europe, and attempts to staunch it with applications of money to a few affected communities hint of King Canute and the waves. It is also sadly ironic if a future for islands where the land is still, as Thomas Balfour observed in 1795, "so happily adapted" to the production of superb cattle, can only be seen in tourism (inevitably limited by the climate), or in light industry or information technology and not in the land at all.

These pages have brought the story of Holland through its past revolutions on the wheel of fortune to its present at the beginning of the 21st century. Forecasting the future is for economists, consultants and astrologers; for the farmer the present moment is simply too urgent a concern to indulge in crystal ball gazing. Our agricultural destinies have largely been taken out of our own hands and put into those of politicians but, to wonder what they will do with them, "that way madness lies". It is not the latest EU directive or bulletin of regulations from MAFF that we are awaiting at Holland but the grass seed on the steamer[7] for re-sowing fields cultivated for the last 6,000 years. Today's depressing news is not a fall in cattle prices but the collapse of another section of Traill's 150-year-old dyke that urgently needs repair. In the midst of lambing and calving our anxiety is not for our economic viability but our ability to keep awake for the next birth. While it is impossible at the moment to be sanguine about the future of farming upon which we depend, it is, fortunately, the present needs of the creatures dependent upon us that overwhelm our attention. In the winter darkness of the byre shelter the next generation of Holland's calves that in spring will play in the hoofprints of their remote ancestors, around the Knap of Howar on the Links of Holland.

While the earth remaineth, seedtime and harvest shall not cease.
Genesis 8 v 22

Circles everywhere.

Everything that sets out must complete a journey.

What appears to us voyagers a tangle, random blunderings,

Is seen angel-vantaged, as certain as the star-wheel

Or the journey from a root that ends in the June rose.

The seed, the bequest, will quicken again under snow.

George Mackay Brown "Swans at Brodgar"

Dusk, and another Holmie Day comes to an end.

Glossary

I have used the farming terms in current use on Papay. Most of these will be common to other areas of Scotland, especially the north-east, but a few may now be restricted to the North Isles of Orkney and unfamiliar. Some of the terms quoted from documents, especially the weights and measures used in the old Rentals and the 19th-century Rent Books, are now obsolete but occur frequently in source material.

Bere, bear — A more primitive and hardy form of barley, formerly grown all over Orkney

Caisie — Straw basket carried on back, used for *kelp*, peats etc

Coles — Small cones in which the hay is loosely piled in the field for further drying before being carried to the yard and built into haystacks

Corn — *Bere*

Cruive — Sheepfold

Dyke — Wall; early dykes were usually of turf (fealy dykes), or turf and stones, but the enclosure dykes of the 18th and 19th centuries were built of drystone walling

Feu Duties — Annual payment made by landholder to feudal superior, traditionally paid in kind (usually grain and butter in Orkney) but in the 19th century commuted to a fixed money payment

Gairsty — A (prehistoric) earthen dyke, see *treb dyke*

Grieve — Farm foreman

Hairst — Harvest

Hanseatic League or *Hansa*; organisation founded by north German towns and commercial groups abroad which established trading bases in many foreign towns and protected their trading interests with monopolies; an important political and economic force in northern Europe from the 13th to the 15th century

Holm — Small island, usually uninhabited but used for sheep-grazing and (in the past) *kelp*-making

Kelp — Seaweed reduced by burning to a solidified slag from which soda can be obtained (important in the soap- and glass-making industry), and also iodine

Kirk Session — Minister and elders of a presbyterian church, which form its administrative and disciplinary body

Kye — Cows

Leading — The sheaves of oats or corn are "led" from the field to the stackyard at the *hairst*

Lispund — Unit of weight used only for butter, especially for payment of rents and *skat.* In 1824 the lispund was defined as 26.625 lbs, but it was probably significantly less at the time of Lord Henry's Rental

Malt — *Bere* that has been prepared for brewing by being steeped and then allowed to take heat until germination starts, then dried in the kiln

Mark, Merk — Unit of currency, equivalent to £ 2/3, used in valuing land; also a unit of weight for grain, meat etc. 24 merks = 1 setting or *lispund*

Meil	Unit of weight, 6 settings = 1 meil, 24 meils = 1 last These weights are used in deeds relating to rents and feus well into the 20th century; they are hard to translate exactly into imperial measures as different commodities were weighed on different types of weighing-beam (the Malt Pundlar, Bere Pundlar and Bismar) using different weights, see Appendix I
Mill tramp	Circular area "tramped" by the horses powering the engine which drove a threshing mill. Elsewhere, mill course, horse course, horse engine, horse gang etc
Neeps	Turnips
Onca	(Lit. "on call"), casual labour services paid by a tenant in addition to rent
Ouzen	Ox, bullock
Pattie	Pig
Peedie, peerie	Small
Pennyland	Unit of land, defined by value rather than acreage for taxation purposes
Plough-sock	Plough-share
Quey	Normally written as such but pronounced "quoyo" in Papay, a heifer
Run-rig	The commonly used Scottish term for the landholding system that was known as "rig and rendal" in Orkney, by which tenants of a communal farm held their arable land in strips in each township field rather than in a single field or block of land
Segs	Wild irises
Shearing	Reaping
Skat, scat	Land tax
Staig, staigy	Stallion
Stilt	Handle of plough
Stirk	Young bullock or heifer
Stook	Sheaves (of oats or corn), were first "stooked" in the field in groups of six sheaves for further drying before being led to the yard for building into a stack
Stot	Bullock
Swap	To catch birds in a hand net
Treb dyke	Bronze Age earthworks, also known as *gairstys*, eg the Muckle Gairsty in North Ronaldsay
Udallers	Owners of private property, with no feudal superior
Urisland	An administrative district, defined for taxation purposes and subdivided into eighteen *pennylands*; also ounceland
Weigh, wey	Unit of weight used for *kelp*; kelp weights were variable and always subject to negotiation and change, but the wey was eventually standardised at two hundredweights

Note on Spelling

The spelling of place-names on the island varies widely in maps and documents and often several variants are in current use. In quotations I have retained the original spelling, but elsewhere I have used the version most commonly used today.

Appendix I

Papay in Lord Henry's Rental

Almost the only sources of information for the history of Orkney in the late medieval period are the Rentals and the earliest of these to survive is that drawn up by Lord Henry Sinclair in 1492. In 1479/80 Lord Henry inherited from his grandfather Earl William Sinclair what was left of his Orkney estate after he had sold most of it to James III. In 1490 Henry acquired the tack of the Crown lands in Orkney and so he was managing these (which included Papay) in addition to his own estate. When he took stock of his affairs in 1492, Orkney was undergoing the long-term agricultural depression which caused the abandonment of villages and arable land all over northern Europe. Not only had much of his farmland fallen out of cultivation due to the economic crisis, but large portions of the North Isles had been destroyed by serious sea-erosion or sand-blow. In 1492 Lord Henry was visiting his estate to assess the amount of damaged land and to re-evaluate the sums to be paid in rent and *skat* (land tax).

These were levied in agricultural produce and money and paid in butter, oil, grain or meat according to a fixed rate of values, *pennyworths:*

1 lispund of butter	=	4 skat pennies
1 setten of bere	=	4 skat pennies
1 setten of malt	=	6 skat pennies
1 setten of flesche	=	6 skat pennies

Skat was traditionally paid principally in butter, but by this time it had become accepted that only a proportion (about 1/5, the *stent*) was paid in real butter and the remainder in its value of grain or meat. There was also a *malt skat* (paid in bere in Papay, malt in Westray), *forcop* (usually assessed as a sum of money, and in Papay apparently paid that way, although in other places it was often paid in grain) and *wattle* (originally an obligation to provide hospitality for the earl and his retainers when they were travelling around the islands, but by 1492 converted to a fixed payment). Rent had originally been expressed entirely in terms of grain but in the late Middle Ages, as grain-growing tended to give way to a more pastoral economy, meat came to be accepted according to a recognised scale of grain-equivalents. By Lord Henry's time grain was an over-supplied market and where possible he preferred payment in the more marketable animal products, salted meat, fish- or seal-oil, and butter, all valuable commodities which he could export to markets in the south.

Unfortunately the Papay rental is less detailed than most. The island is treated as two administrative divisions, each valued for taxation purposes as two *urislands*, but the rental is not itemised for individual farms as it is in other parishes. So one cannot discover the produce paid by Holland Farm to Lord Henry, but it is possible to glean a little information about medieval Papay as a whole. An urisland contained 18 *pennylands* and so there were 72 pennylands of taxable land in the island. These were a unit of value and their acreage varied, but the pennylands in the North Isles tended to be smaller than those on Mainland, typically between five and ten acres in extent. This suggests that these areas were densely settled at an early stage of Norse colonisation, probably because the light sandy soils were relatively easily cultivated by primitive ploughs. The pennylands are also a clue to the amount of cultivated land at the time. They contained both arable and pasture land, and so 72 ten-acre pennylands probably represent less than 700 acres of arable ground. The rents and skats were therefore paid out of the produce of well under half the present area of arable land in the island.

Almost all the island fell within the Earldom estate, just 3½ pennylands belonging to the Bishopric estate, ("in Kirk mennis hands"). Two-fifths of the island was *udal* land, private property which paid no rent, and this was presumably the situation until the Traills came to the island in the 17th century and succeeded in acquiring all the udal land and reducing everyone else to tenant status.

In 1492 Lord Henry was told that one-quarter of the land in Papay had been so destroyed by erosion or sand-blow that it was deemed worthless and relieved of the obligation to pay skat, ("the fourt part blawin that pays richt nocht") and large portions of Westray had been similarly devastated. In a picturesque comment he reported that the land was "blawn til Issland"! Evidently this was long-term damage, for in the 1500 Rental there are still 9 pennylands in Papay "all our blawin with wattir et sand". There was also 5 pennylands of ley land which had fallen temporarily out of cultivation but which Lord Henry hoped to let out on advantageous terms ("the malt scat and forcop . . . stricken down") so that it would be farmed again. He encouraged the farmers on his estate to take up the abandoned land by reducing rent and skat and under his good management much of this ley land was gradually brought back into cultivation. His tacksman, Brandy Drever, for example, was given a life-rent of one pennyland of ley land in Papay be-south the yard rent-free to encourage him to farm it.. Brandy was expected to pay the skat, and for the privilege of trapping the rabbits for their valuable skins he paid "for the Linx . . .7 score cunning skinns". Since the rents and skats are assessed on the whole district, "be-north" and "be-south", it would have been Brandy's job to assess the contribution of each farm, and to collect the produce at the appropriate time.

There is an interesting difference between the rate of rent paid by the two districts. In the south half we find that the renting rate is 4 marks to the pennyland (at 10 settens to the mark), the most common renting rate, but in the north the rate is only half this, about 2 marks to the pennyland, which is unusually low. The presence of a number of man-made structures below the high-tide level at North Wick suggest that a considerable amount of land has been "drowned" here at some stage, and it is a tantalising possibility that this low rental of be-north the yard relates to the particularly severe devastation of this end of the island. However, there is no evidence for dating these structures to the medieval period.

It seems that the butter skat had previously been related more closely to the numbers of livestock which the land supported, rather than standardised at the rate of a span (tub) per three pennylands as it was by the late 15th century. At the beginning of the Westray rental we read that Lord Henry asked the leading farmers how the stent butter was paid in times past. They said that every newly calved cow had paid half a lispund of butter yearly, but Henry "understud thare poverty" and agreed to take one lispund from every three pennylands and the rest of "the butter scat of unblawn land to be paid in pennyworthis sic as growis upon the ground". So much of the butter payment was actually made in grain.

The units of weight were:

24 merks	=	1 lispund (butter only) or setten
6 settens	=	1 meil
24 meils	=	1 last

In 1826 these old weights and measures were standardised to imperial equivalents:

1 lispund	=	29 lbs 10 oz 12 drachms
1 meil on the malt pundlar	=	177 lbs 12 oz
1 meil on the bere pundlar	=	116 lbs 7 oz

However, the Orkney weights had been unscrupulously tampered with over the centuries to increase the amount of rent and skats collected and it is estimated that they increased by as much as 2½ times from the 12th to the 18th century, (a process that was common to the rest of Scotland). This means, unfortunately, that it is impossible to translate the traditional weights into imperial measures with any degree of accuracy, but some very rough approximations can be attempted.

Lord Henry summarised the Papay skats and rents paid annually as:

The stent (paid in real butter)	=	16 lispund 22 merks
The forcop (paid in silver)		15 shillings 3d

3 scat merts (3 cattle ready for slaughter at Martinmas)

(The rest of the payments were probably paid in grain and can be translated into their equivalent value of bere):

The rest of the butter skat 22 shillings 6d	=		11 meils 2½ settens
The bere skat	=	1 last	21 meils 4½ settens
Rent in bere	=	3 lasts	6 meils
Rent in flesch 1 last 21 meils 2 settens	=	2 lasts	20 meils
15 meils pennyworthis	=		15 meils
watill	=		9 meils
Total			226 meils bere

If the weights used in Lord Henry's time had been increased 2½ times by the time of the 1826 standardisation, 1 meil of bere would have been equivalent to 46½ lbs in 1492, and the island paying 94 hundred-weight, or nearly five tons of grain annually in rent and tax, besides the fairly heavy payment in silver and the three fat cattle. The stent, on the same calculation, would have been 504 lbs of butter. These quantities of produce could probably be met quite easily in good years, (a single 13 acre farm on Papay paid 75lbs of butter in rent in 1844). The problem was that the traditional system of levying rents and skat in Orkney allowed for no flexibility in times of economic or climatic crisis: fixed amounts had to be found annually whether the harvest was good or a total failure, so in a good year the tacksman took the surplus produce that might have insured against hunger in the next.

Appendix II

Orkney's Imports and Exports 1805 - 1806

IMPORTS

536 galls port wine
198 galls sherry
6,120 lbs snuff
4,481 lbs tea
7 bolls beremeal
70 cwt raw wool
1 qr 6 bushels pease
3 tons oak bark
205 cwt drest hemp
2,0178 soft soap
38 gross empty bottles
18 cwt gingerbread
6,900 bricks
368 galls rum
10,492½ galls British spirits
35 galls brandy
12 cwt dye-stuffs
12 chests, 20 boxes, 24 packs & 216 bales haberdashery
127 tons coals
344 lbs rosin
1,501 lbs tallow candles
15 galls green oil
3 bundles spades
6 casks whitening
3 hogsheads linseed
2 casks, 2 boxes oilmen's ware
25 lbs glue
2 casks ashes
10½ doz corn riddles
5 load 26 feet 3 pieces ash, elm & beech
12 pints honey
10 tons whale oil
6 barrels white herrings
163 cwt refined sugar
120 cwt raw sugar
1,544 lbs tobacco
95 cwt hulled barley
22 qrs malt
608 cwt tow
703 yds canvas
118½ tanned leather
297 cwt undrest flax
82 cwt hardware
56 cwt unwrought iron
248 bundles wooden hoops
8 parcels saddlery ware
381 galls gin
600 pieces fir timber
526 cwt drest flax
399 lbs alum
33 doz wool cards
4 cwt cheese
361 chalders coals
2 parcels & 1 box apothecary's ware
2 casks mustard
80 pair cartwheels
10 cartloads household furniture
7 qrs, 2 bushels, 8 sacks rye grass & clover seeds*
200 tyles
3 cwt candy sugar
29 lbs twine
62 lbs thread
3 cwt lead
600 deals
2 cwt rosin
24 bags cork
197 cwt flour
368 cwt biscuits
2061 bushels salt
23 bolls oatmeal
2 bolls potatoes
148 cwt molasses
166 cwt cordage
197 barrels tar
162 cwt hard soap
338 cwt wrought iron
12 bundles lathwood
97 crates earthenware
20 boxes tinware
84½ cwt hops
35 loads & 7 tons oak timber
5½ cwt nails
25 bales stationery
50 boxes glass
27 casks strong beer
49 chalders cinders
82 galls vinegar
39 boxes hats
3 boxes tobacco pipes
209 hogsheads porter
22 galls spruce beer
1 bottle turpentine
21 bushels apples
2 carts complete
52 empty barrels
25 tons freestone
10 cwt confections
25 cwt lead shot
16 cwt groceries
900 hazel cuts

*(The reference to the rye grass and clover seeds is particularly interesting, suggesting that some Orkney farms had started to sow artificial grasses half a century before it became common practice in the county).

EXPORTS

2,272 tons kelp
204 barrels butter
17,310 spindles linen yarn
5 barrels pork
1,620 yds woollen stuff
479 cwt ling & cod
2,000 slates
7 cwt cow hair
9 otter skins
5 boxes eggs
636 salted hides
37,014 yds linen cloth
812 doz rabbit skins
20 cwt & 1 hogshead pork hams
163 barrels oatmeal
87 oxen & cows (alive)
$26^{1}/_{2}$ cwt raw wool
90 cwt feathers
78 barrels beef
171 doz calf skins
101,000 goose quills
$5^{1}/_{2}$ cwt tallow
63 barrels fish-oil
3,133 qrs bere
540 galls ale
16 cwt tanned leather
39,000 dried sillock

These lists, derived from the Customs and Excise records, are based on Shirreff. They indicate the type of merchandise that merchant lairds such as the Traills were engaged in trading between Orkney and the ports of Britain and northern Europe, and shed an interesting light on the economy of the county in the early 19th century. The much longer list of imports, including the expensive luxury items such as spirits, suggests a considerable trade imbalance which was only rectified in the 1840s when the improving steamship service allowed Orkney to start exporting livestock in quantity. The number of live cattle exported rose from 87 in 1805 to 1,580 in 1848 and 7,340 in 1866. In 1995 they totalled 22,951.

Bibliography and Abbreviations

BARCLAY, R.S., *The Population of Orkney 1755-1961,* Kirkwall 1965

DAFS = Department of Agriculture and Fisheries, Agricultural Returns, 1866 onward

DENNISON, W.T., Remarks on the Agricultural Classes in the North Isles of Orkney 1883, repr. *POAS* XII, 1933

DICKSON, J., Some Account of the Orkney Islands, *Transactions of the Highland and Agricultural Society of Scotland,* Edinburgh 1841

FARRALL, T., On the Agriculture of Orkney, *Transactions of the Highland and Agricultural Society of Scotland,* Edinburgh 1874

FEA, J., *The Present State of the Orkney Islands Considered* (1775), 1884

FENTON, A., *The Northern Isles; Orkney and Shetland,* Edinburgh 1978

FENTON, A., & WALKER, B., *The Rural Architecture of Scotland,* Edinburgh 1981

FEREDAY, R.P., *Orkney Feuds and the '45,* Kirkwall 1980

FEREDAY, R.P., The Lairds and 18th-Century Orkney, in Berry, R. J., and Firth, H. N., ed., *The People of Orkney*, Kirkwall 1986

FIRTH, J., *Reminiscences of an Orkney Parish,* Stromness 1974

HANDLEY, J.E., *Scottish Farming in the 18th Century,* London 1953

HAY, G.D., & STELL, G.P., *Monuments of Industry,* Edinburgh 1986

HEPBURN, T., (attrib.) *Letter to a Gentleman from his friend in Orkney (*1760), 1885

HEWISON, W.S., Holm Farm Diary 1849-68, *Orkney Miscellany* II, 1954

HEWISON, W.S., Smuggling in 18th Century Orkney, *Orkney Miscellany* III, 1956

HEWISON, W.S., ed., *The Diary of Patrick Fea of Stove 1766-96*, East Linton 1997

HOSSACK, B.H., *Kirkwall in the Orkneys,* Kirkwall 1900

HRB = Holland Rent Books (1844-1884)

JOADS = Journals of the Orkney Agricultural Discussion Society

LAMB, R.G., *The Archeological Sites and Monuments of Scotland: Papa Westray and Westray,* RCAHMS 1983

LAMB, R.G., Papil, Picts and Papar, in Crawford, B., ed., *Northern Isles Connections - Essays from Orkney and Shetland presented to Per Sveas Andersen,* Kirkwall 1995

LAMB, R.G., Carolingian Orkney and its Transformations, in Batey, C.E., Jesch, J., and Morris, C.D., *The Viking Age in Caithness Orkney and the North Atlantic - Select Papers from the Proceedings of the 11th Viking Congress,* Edinburgh 1993

LENEMAN, L., *Fit for Heroes? Land Settlement in Scotland after World War I,* Aberdeen 1989

LOW, G., A Tour through the North Isles and part of the Mainland of Orkney in the year 1778, *Old-Lore Miscellany* VIII, 1915

LOWE, C., *Coastal Erosion and the Archaeological Assessment of an Eroding Shoreline at St Boniface Church, Papa Westray, Orkney,* Stroud 1928

MACKAY, J.D., *Farming on Papa Westray in 1920* (OA D1/35/1)

MACKAY, J.D., *Education in Papa Westray 1915-24* (OA D1/35/1)

MACKAY, J.D., *Portrait of William Traill* (OA D31/20/4)

MACKAY, J.D., *Social and Economic Conditions on 19th Century Papa Westray* (OA D31/2/2)

MACKINTOSH, W.R., *The Orkney Crofters; their Evidence and Statements,* Kirkwall 1889

MARWICK, H.M., Antiquarian Notes on Papa Westray, *POAS* III, 1924-25

MARWICK, H.M., Two Orkney 18th Century Inventories, *POAS* XII, 1933-34

MARWICK, H.M., *Merchant Lairds of Long Ago*, Kirkwall 1939

MILLER, R., ed., *The 3rd Statistical Account of Scotland, XXA The County of Orkney,* Edinburgh 1985

Minute Book of the Papa Westray Parish Council 1895-1914, (OA C06/11)

MOIRA, R.E. and B.L.C., *County Survey of Orkney, Part I The North Isles,* 1960

NAPIER = Napier Commission Report, *Evidence taken by Her Majesty's Commission of Inquiry into the Condition of the Crofters and Cottars in the Highlands and Islands of Scotland,* 1884

NEIL, P., *A Tour through some of the Islands of Orkney and Shetland,* Edinburgh 1806

NIPR = North Isles Presbytery Records, (OA OCR/3/1)

NSA = New Statistical Account, *The Statistical Account of the Orkney Islands,* Edinburgh 1842

OA = Orkney Archives

O'DELL, A.C., *The Land of Britain, Part IV Orkney*, London 1939

OMOND, J., *Orkney Eighty Years Ago*, Kirkwall 1911

The Orcadian

The Orkney Herald

ORWIN, C.S., and WHETHAM, E., *A History of British Agriculture 1846-1914,* Newton Abbott 1971

OSA = Old Statistical Account, STORER CLOUSTON, J., *The Orkney Parishes,* Kirkwall 1928, (selected repr. of Sinclair, J., ed., *The Statistical Account of Scotland* 1791-99)

PALSSON, H., and EDWARDS, E., tr., *Orkneyinga Saga,* Harmondsworth 1981

Papa Westray Parish Census 1841-1891, (OA)

PERREN, R., *Agriculture in Depression 1870-1940,* Cambridge 1995

PETERKIN, A., *Rentals of the Ancient Earldom & Bishoprick of Orkney,* Edinburgh 1820

POAS = Proceedings of the Orkney Antiquarian Society

PRINGLE, R.O., On the Agriculture of the Islands of Orkney, *Transactions of the Highland and Agricultural Society of Scotland*, Edinburgh 1874

RENDALL, J., *Papay,* Papa Westray 1992, repr.1996

RENDALL, J., *A History of St Boniface Kirk,* Papa Westray 1994

RS = Register of Sasines (Register House, Edinburgh)

SC = Session Court Records (Orkney Archives)

SCARTH, R., and WATT, G., Agriculture of Orkney, *Transactions of the Highland and Agricultural Society,* Edinburgh 1939

SCHRANK, G., *An Orkney Estate: Improvements at Graemeshall, 1827-1888,* East Linton 1995

SEMPLE, J.F., *Orkney Farming Survey. Farming Trends, Report No.1,* HIDB 1966

SENIOR, W.H., SWAN, W.B., *Survey of Agriculture in Caithness, Orkney and Shetland, Special Report 8*, HIDB 1972

SHIRREFF, J., *A General View of the Agriculture of the Orkney Islands,* Edinburgh 1814

SINCLAIR, J., *A General View of the Agriculture of the Northern Counties and Islands of Scotland,* 1795

SINCLAIR, J., *Preliminary Reports,* 1795

SINCLAIR, J., *General Report of the Agricultural State of Scotland,* 1814

SLICHER VAN BATH, B.H., *The Agrarian History of Western Europe AD 500-1850,* London 1963

SRO = Scottish Record Office

THOMSON, William P.L., *The Little General and the Rousay Crofters,* Edinburgh 1981

THOMSON, William P.L., *Kelp Making in Orkney,* Kirkwall 1983

THOMSON, William P.L., 15th Century Depression in Orkney: the Evidence of Lord Henry Sinclair's Rentals, in Crawford, B.E., *Essays in Shetland History,* Lerwick 1984
THOMSON, William P.L., St Findan and the Pictish-Norse Transition, in Berry, R. J., and Firth, H. N., ed., *The People of Orkney,* Kirkwall 1986
THOMSON, William P.L., *A History of Orkney*, Edinburgh 1987
THOMSON, William P.L., *Lord Henry Sinclair's 1492 Rental of Orkney,* Kirkwall 1996
THOMSON, William P.L., *The New History of Orkney,* Edinburgh 2001
TRAILL, Walter, *Vindication of Orkney,* Edinburgh 1823
TRAILL, William, *Genealogical Account of the Traills of Orkney,* Kirkwall 1883
Valuation Rolls for the County of Orkney
WALLACE, J., *Description of the Isles of Orkney* (1693), Edinburgh 1883

References

Preface

1. I am indebted to Dr Ian Simpson for information on the way that sophisticated techniques of soil analysis are being used to study early farming practice. In his paper "Transitions in early arable land management in the Northern Isles - the *papar* as agricultural innovators" delivered to the Fifth St Andrews Dark Age Studies conference, 2001, Dr Simpson suggested that it was the Christian *papar* or clergy who first pioneered techniques of intensive manuring with turf and dung, and introduced these to the North Atlantic settlements.
2. IACS = Integrated Administration and Control Scheme, introduced in 1994. The payment of agricultural subsidy is conditional on the farmer completing an annual IACS return, which provides the government with a detailed record of the hectareage owned or rented by each farm and the crops grown on it. One purpose of IACS is to control livestock numbers: "extensification payment" encourages farmers to keep less animals by paying subsidy at a higher rate to farms with a lower density of stock per hectare.
   CAP = Common Agricultural Policy (of the European Union)
   BSE = Bovine Spongiform Encephalopathy or "mad cow" disease, the outbreaks in the 1990s and their effects on farming are referred to in chap.XI

Chapter I - Island

A most beautiful little isle . . ., The Rev George Low "A Tour through the North Isles and part of the Mainland of Orkney in the year 1778"

1. Lamb 1983, 7-8; 1993; Rendall 1994, 1-8
2. Rendall 1996, 30-34
3. Lowe 1998, 11
4. Lamb 1995, 22; Thomson 2001, 21
5. *Orkneyinga Saga* 71, 102, 128
6. Thomson 1984, 1996. The agricultural crisis of the 15th century was so severe that villages were abandoned all over France, Germany, England, Spain, Scandinavia and the Netherlands.
7. Thomson 1996, 60
8. Peterkin 1820, 85; Thomson 1996, 63. In 1492 the tacksman of Westray and Papay, Brandy Drever, paid a rent of 140 rabbit-skins for the Links. Assuming this represents a small proportion of the expected harvest of the Links, the original occupants of the skins were quite plentiful enough to cause an erosion problem.
9. For a more detailed analysis of the evidence for the Papay economy in Lord Henry's Rental, see Appendix I
10. Low, 149
11. OSA, 340
12. Neill, 41

Chapter II - Lairds

Traills up the town . . . Traditional

1. Hossack, 157. The name Traill has now disappeared from Orkney.
2. Marwick, 1924
3. SRO, RS43/5 f.226ff
4. *Ancient Orkney Melodies Collected by Col David Balfour of Balfour,* Edinburgh 1885, repr. By The Orkney Press, Kirkwall 1985, v
5. SRO, RS43/6 ff.51.65.125; RS43/7 f.111; RS43/8 f.85

6. OSA, 337
7. Document relating to feu duties inherited by Thomas Traill, OA SC11/5/1725/14
8. NIPR 1719-20, OCR 3/1, 50-61, 85-90
9. NIPR 1719, OCR 3/1, 51-52
10. Fereday 1980, viii
11. Fereday 1980. 29
12. NIPR 1720, OCR 3/1, 90
13. NIPR 1719, OCR 3/1, 59
14. Fereday 1980, 119-119
15. OA, SC11/5/1769/53
16. Wallace, 12
17. Appendix II reproduces in full Shirreff's list of Orkney's exports and imports for the year 1805-06.
18. Letter from Thomas Smith, Breck, Westray to William Watt, Hewison 1956
19. Low, 150
20. Shirreff, 147.
21. Shirreff, Appendix XVIII, "*Modes of catching Sea Fowl on the Cliffs and in the Goes in the Islands of Westray and Papay Westray*"
22. Neill, 43
23. Pringle, 36
24. OA, RS 14 January 1868
25. OA, RS 12 November 1880
26. OA, Register of Sequestrations 15 July 1886

Chapter III - A Wretched State of Agriculture

Our agriculture . . ., Colonel Thomas Balfour, in John Sinclair *Preliminary Reports,* 1795

1. Fenton 1978, 333-334
2. OSA, 340
3. Hewison 1997
4. Dennison, 51
5. Mackintosh, 137
6. NIPR 1719, OCR 3/1, 50
7. Thomson, 1981, 40
8. Richard Hakluyt, *Voyages and Discoveries*, 1600, ed. Beeching, J., Harmondsworth 1972, 188
9. Dennison, 54
10. G & P Anderson, *Guide to the Highlands & Islands of Scotland* 1850, 680
11. Hepburn, 16
12. Hepburn, 16-18
13. Firth, 22
14. *Memorial for the Heritors and other inhabitants of the Orkney Islands* 1784, OA D24/9/1
15. Fea, 44
16. Sinclair 1795, *Preliminary Reports*, 236
17. Shirreff 1814
18. Marwick, 1933, 50.
19. Dennison, 52
20. Dickson, 116
21. Dennison, 53
22. James Flett, "The Orkney Agricultural Society", *POAS* XII 1933, 43-44

23. OSA, 341
24. Neill, 32
25. Scarth & Watt, 4

Chapter IV - The Golden Age

Landscape plotted and pieced. . ., Gerard Manley Hopkins "Pied Beauty", *Poems* 1875-89

1. Shirreff, 144
2. George Traill added Rapness to the Holland estate in 1831, buying it from the Trustees of Captain William Richan who died in 1829 having gone bankrupt when kelp prices collapsed.
3. NSA, 118
4. NSA, 121
5. NSA, 120
6. NSA, 118,128
7. NSA, 118
8. Traill 1823, 36
9. Fea, 3. "Laying sheep" refers to the practice of smearing sheep with a mixture of tar and butter, thought to act as an insecticide before the invention of chemical sheep-dips.
10. *The Orcadian*, 1865 onward
11. Mackay, OA D31/2/2
12. HRB
13. HRB
14. Brough Cash Book 1870
15. Orwin and Whetham, 259
16. Perren, 13
17. Pringle, 36
18. Pringle, 32
19. HRB
20. DAFS
21. Pringle, 37
22. HRB
23. Pringle, 36
24. Schrank, 57-8
25. Application to the Crofters' Commission 1888 by Thomas Harcus, Midhouse (private collection)
26. HRB
27. Farrall, 92

ChapterV - Worthy of his Hire

Seventy years I've had. . ., George Mackay Brown "Farm Labourer", *Selected Poems 1954-1992,* John Murray 1996, quoted by kind permission of the publisher and G M Brown's executors

1. Papa Westray Parish Census 1841-91
2. HRB
3. Letter from John Baikie to Andrew Drever 1864 (private collection)
4. HRB

Chapter VI - End of an Era

*The farmer ploughed. . .*Edwin Muir, "The Breaking", *Collected Poems,* Faber and Faber 1960, quoted by kind permission of the publisher

1. Papa Westray Parish Council Minutes

2. *The Orkney Herald*, 26 June 1889
3. *The Orkney Herald*, 9 October 1889
4. *The Orkney Herald* , 30 August 1899
5. *The Orkney Herald*, 22 August 1900
6. Papa Westray Parish Council Minutes
7. Mackay, OA D1/35/1
8. OA RS 8 November 1922
9. *The Orkney Herald* , 7 June 1922
10. Thomson 1987, 242
11. Thomson, 1987, 241

Chapter VII - Crofters

Parliament robs me... General FW Burroughs, letter to Charles Traill, 1888

1. Napier, 1533-1583
2. Mackintosh, v-vi
3. Ibid, 176-193
4. The Crofters Holdings (Scotland) Act 1886, Mackintosh 277ff
5. Mackintosh, 193-197
6. Letter from General Burroughs to Charles Traill of Ulva, 1888, OA D1/113
7. *Answers for William Cursiter, Charleston and others, in application for Enlargement of Holdings, Record No.1132, to General Statements and Objections lodged by Mr Drever for William Baird Esq of Elie landlord and Thomas Cumming Esq Tenant of Holland Farm*, OA
8. OA D7/4/1
9. Leneman *passim*
10. Application by the Board of Agriculture for Scotland to the Scottish Land Court, Record No. 1530
11. Ibid, Record No.1529
12. Holland papers

Chapter VIII - A Commodious Farm Steading

Nothing contributes more . . . Dr James Anderson, *General View of the Agriculture of Aberdeenshire,* 1794

1. E. Beaton, *The Doocots of Moray,* Moray 1978, 1
2. NIPR 1719, OCR 3/1, 50
3. Robert Rendall, "The Horse-Mill" published in *Orkney Variants* by The Kirkwall Press 1951
4. Document referring to feu duties inherited by Thomas Traill, 3rd of Holland, from his grandfather, OA SC 11/5/1723/4
5. Pringle, 84

Chapter IX - Hard Times and Iron Horses

Wooden harvesters... 19th century American, in B H Slicher van Bath, *The Agrarian History of Western Europe AD 500-1850*

1. Perren, 31
2. Perren, 33
3. Perren, 37
4. Perren, 41-42, 55
5. Thomson 1987, 242

6. OA RS 8 August 1923
7. Mackay, OA D31/20/4
8. Valuation Rolls 1881-1941
9. *The Orkney Herald*, 4 December 1918. Wages fell again after the repeal of the Corn Production Act in 1921. The first Labour government reintroduced statutory wages legislation in England and Wales with the Agricultural Wages (Regulation) Act in 1924. Scotland had no wages legislation until 1937.
10. "The Horse v Mechanical Traction", *JOADS* VI 1931
11. Miller, 248

Chapter X - *Of Beasts and Men*

The winter lift. . .Robert Rendall, "Celestial Kinsmen", *Orkney Variants,* The Kirkwall Press, 1951

1. O'Dell, 251; Scarth & Watt, 4
2. Thomson 1987, 245
3. Scarth & Watt, 13
4. DAFS
5. Semple, Appendix V
6. Ibid
7. Miller, 249
8. Semple, 13, Appendix VII, VIII
9. Semple, 12
10. DAFS
11. Miller, xi
12. Senior & Swan, 44

Chapter XI - On Fortune's Wheel

No meet honour. . . Virgil, *The Georgics* Book I, c.36 B.C.

1. Semple, 15
2. P. Maxwell, "Silage", *JOADS* I, 1925
3. *Orkney Economic Review*, 1981
4. Report *New Entrants to Land Markets*, quoted in *The Scotsman* 7th January 2001
5. Slicher van Bath, 165
6. Minute Book of Papa Westray Committee of North Isles Association
7. The North Isles ferry boats ceased to be literally steam-powered in 1979; the name endures.

Index

The Author

Brought up in a service family which was constantly on the move, since 1989 Jocelyn Rendall has lived and worked on Holland Farm which has been home to her husband's family for over 80 years. After a number of jobs ranging from caring for handicapped children in Switzerland to being a barmaid in the Outer Hebrides and a stockhand on a sheep station in Central Queensland, she took an MA in medieval art at Edinburgh University and subsequently worked as curator of the Mackintosh Collection at the Glasgow School of Art. It was the chance to join the team excavating a chambered cairn on the Holm of Papay which first brought her to the island. She is the author of articles on early Byzantine textile design, *Charles Rennie Mackintosh, Papay, St Boniface Kirk,* and *Papay in Focus.* Addicted to travelling and to mountains, she wrote *A Jar of Seed-Corn* as a thanks for the small flat place which is home.